ADVANCED COMPUTER AIDED

MANUFACTURING APPLICATIONS

Using INVENTOR CAM

For CNC Milling

Pavel Ikonomov Ph. D.

Preface

This book is created to help users of Inventor CAM software and CNC machines to develop programs for CNC machines. Major topics are programming of CNC machines using standard G and M code command using Inventor CAM. Each command is explained in detail and presented with detailed subsequent images for each small step to reduce possible misinterpretations. An effort was made to explain commands, programming sequences, and requirements while keeping the description minimum.

In my teaching experience, using CAM for CNC machining was the most challenging part of any Computer Aided Manufacturing, Computer Integrated Manufacturing process, and CNC programming laboratory. This tutorial was originally written for students in the College of Engineering and Applied Sciences to help them with a group of courses: Introduction to Machine processes - EDMM 2540, Metrology-EDMM 3540, Computer Aided Manufacturing - EDMM 3580, Manufacturing System Integration – EDMM 4580, Concurrent Engineering - EDMM 5460, and Computer Aided Manufacturing Applications - EDMM 6580.

EDMM 4580, EDMM 6580, and EDMM 5460 are advanced courses taken by senior undergraduate and graduate students and require extensive CAD /CAM manufacturing competence. EDMM 2540, EDMM 3540, and EDMM 3580 are attended by students with a broad range of CAD/CAM experience, some with extensive, others with only the introductory programming experience and computer skills. This tutorial is easy to follow even for a user with limited CNC programming experience while at the same time providing support to advanced users.

Detailed descriptions of all the possible program situations for one software with different CNC machines within a single book volume is impossible. For any additional information, users can refer to operation and programming CNC manuals, Inventor CAD manuals, Inventor CAM software help files, and on-line help from CAM vendors. Also, notice that different versions and license schema by CNC or CAM companies may show different results from the one explained in this tutorial. The CNC code was created from post processing setup for machines included in the software. For specific post processor software (plugin), refer to the manufacturer of your CNC machine.

The chapters in this book are not meant to be followed sequentially, so please use the chapter you need for a specific command and programming method. This book is not a reference guide and is intended to give sufficient (but not complete) descriptions of CAM-based CNC programming.

All of the examples shown in this book were individually created. Any similarity of objects, parts, and drawings used in this tutorial are coincidental and unintentional. Files created for this tutorial will be available as a free download on a Website specified by the author.
Access to the site with all the free files from the tutorial needs to be requested from the author. Due to the file sizes, E-mailing of the program files is not practical. *Books samples for each chapter are available at web site:http://homepages.wmich.edu/~pikonomo/*

About the author

Dr. Pavel Ikonomov is Associate Professor in Engineering Design, Manufacturing and Management Engineering Department at Western Michigan University.

He earned his bachelor's degree from the Technical University of Varna and his first master's degree, M.E. in Mechanical Engineering and Manufacturing Technology, from the Technical University of Varna. His second master's degree, M.S. in Mechanical Engineering, was earned from Muroran Institute of Technology, Japan, and his Ph. D in Precision Manufacturing Engineering from Hokkaido University, Japan.

Dr. Pavel Ikonomov worked for several years as a chief mechanical engineer in a petroleum company and Asst. Professor at the Technical University of Varna - Bulgaria. Later he held positions as CTO at Virtual Reality Center Yokohama - Japan, Associate Professor at Tokyo Metropolitan Institute of Technology - Japan, Visiting Professor at UCLA and National Institute of Standard and Technology (NIST). He has extensive industrial and teaching experience in different countries, university research centers, and companies. Dr. Ikonomov has contributed significantly to the development of new data exchange standards, and worked on establishing the STEP standard at Hokkaido University, Japan, and information exchange between design applications and the virtual environment at NIST. He is considered an expert in CAD/CAM, Virtual Reality simulations for industry and nanomanufacturing, and 3D printing. Dr. Ikonomov had published more than 150 papers in journals, proceedings, chapters in books, and have several patents (latest in hybrid 3D metal printing)

Email:
pavel.ikonomov@wmich.edu
pavel.ikonomov@gmail

Table of Contents

Chapter 4
CNC Milling Programming
47

Chapter 5
CNC Programming with Autodesk Inventor: 83
Introduction to CAD Design

Chapter 6
CNC Programming with Inventor   89
CAM: Introduction to CNC Machining

Chapter 7
CNC Programming with Inventor CAM: 109
Advanced 2D Machining

Chapter 8
CNC Programming with Inventor CAM:
3D Machining

Chapter 9
CNC Programming with Inventor CAM:
Multi-axis Machining

225

Chapter 1

Introduction to
Computer Numerical Control Machining

Why NC?
What is NC?
How NC machining works?

Since it appears NC machining has changed the way we machine products. Initially designed for quality and quantity, they have become an indispensable part of any production process, from a fully automated system as Flexible Manufacturing System (FMS) for multiple variations of parts and products to a single workshop production of unique or customized products. With the advance of computers NC technology itself has developed and become more sophisticated in hardware and software usage while at the same time user interface, the why NC operator deal with NC machine, have been simplified. As a result, complicated parts can be produced using general CAM software. Today almost every significant CAD software company offers CAM integration packages as well. The number of NC machines or CNC as they are called nowadays has increased steadily. Typically, NC produces up to 60% of overall machining operations, even though they are about 20% of the total number machine of machine plans equipped. The standards developed and easy data exchange has contributed considerably to make the CNC machine one of the most widely used means of machining in the global market. The Internet has made CNC production fast, easy, and convenient. You may have a design studio in Detroit, send the CAD design to Mexico, produce the CNC program and sent it to Asia, machine the part there, and ship it to the USA or other markets.

History

Applications in the early stages of the Industrial revolution necessitate the introduction of the form of NC machining. Early effort to automate production was a simple use of pulleys, belts, cams, and others. For example, during the Middle Ages, some churches used rotating drums with preposition fixed pins to control chimes. A type of NC utilizing punching card for creating a range of shapes and patterns in knitting machines was used in England early in the 18th century. Later in the 19th century, automatic playing piano "player piano" was invented with keys move following a pattern of holes in a punched paper scroll. Although, the advantages of the automation, the cheap manual labor, and better quality was a reason to use human to control machines.

During World War II, a shortage of qualified workers and the increased requirements for quantity and quality industry recognize that there is a need for new technology. The war machines such as airplanes, tanks, guns, required high-quality identical parts and high volumes. Highly qualified machinists could produce high-quality parts, but could not meet the manifold increase of quantity. Due to the necessities of war battles, the US Air Force needs many new high-quality identical airplanes to be manufactured with high quality. Several companies have been chosen to develop and manufacture numerical control systems to meet this demand.

The special requirement that NC machines need to meet were:
1. Increase production output together while guarantee high quality and accuracy of parts being produced

2. Stabilize manufacturing cost while parts are manufactured quickly
3. Producing complex parts that were not possible by the conventional manual methods

Figure1.1 NC design was intended to meet the production demand during World War II

The parts produce with NC machines were not aimed at mass production rather flexibility to meet specific production requirements. The production quantities of parts are for small and medium-size batches, with varied sizes and geometry that can be produced with similar steps and settings, see Figure 1.1.

During World War II, the world's first digital computer Electronic Numerical Integrator and Computer - ENIAC was designed and built to calculate artillery firing tables for the U.S. Army's Ballistics Research Laboratory. Project PX was constructed by the University of Pennsylvania's Moore School of Electrical Engineering from July 1943. It was unveiled on February 15, 1946. It contained 17,468 vacuum tubes, weighed 30 short of tons (27 t), and consumed 150 kW of power. In the early '50s, MIT developed a more advanced vacuum tube computer "Whirlwind" that operated in real-time, used video displays for output, and was thousands of times faster in computational instruction than ENIAC.

In 1948, "Parsons Corporation" of Traverse City, Michigan, was awarded a contract from U.S. Air Forces to make tapered wings for military aircraft. Earlier, John T. Parsons (Detroit, October 13, 1913) pioneered numerical control for machine tools in the 1940s. Together, with his employee Frank L. Stulen, they were the first to use computational methods to solve machining problems. It was used for the accurate interpolation of the curves describing helicopter blades.

MIT's servo Mechanism Laboratory was subcontracted in 1951 and later took over the total NC development. The first working NC three-axis numerical controlled machine tool was created at MIT in 1952 and shown to the military, the aerospace industry, the machine tool industry, and the technical media, Figure 1.2. MIT's Whirlwind computer was used to control the three-axis movement on a retrofitted Cincinnati Micron Hydrotel Vertical Spindle milling machine simultaneously. In a few years, most of the machine tool manufacturers start the production of NC machines.

In 1955 a standardization of the Numerical Control system was recommended to Air Force by the subcommittee of the Airspace Industries Association (AIA).

Figure 1.2 The first 3-axis numerical controlled machine – MIT

CNC Programming Language development

G-code developed by the Electronic Industries Alliance (EIA) in the early 1960s is a common name for the programming language that controls NC and CNC machine tools. The final revision of the standard RS274D was approved in 1980. Most NC/CNC machine tools today can be run using programs written in RS274. However, many machine tool companies introduced different implementations, modifications, or additions of the language. As a result, a CNC program that runs on one machine may not run on another, from a different tool maker, without modification.

The newly developed RS274/NGC[1] language has significantly enhanced the program capability further than those of RS274-D.

To simplify the NC programming for complex parts, MIT started developing computerized Automatically Programmed Tool (APT) 1954. It was based on the concept of using English-like words (so-called high-level) language that generates instructions for the CNC machine from geometry description and tool path motion. Subsequently, new versions of APT, APT II in 1968, and APT III in 1961 were released. APT IV version supported complex surface definition for machining. As it evolved, APT became a standard for CAD/CAM CNC system. Further developments of APT for smaller computers were introduced: ADAPT (IBM), MINIAPT (West Germany), FAPT I, and FAPT (France). Today there are virtually hundreds of programming languages, tools, and software based on APT or developed independently.

Table 1. APT programming example[2]

```
$$ DEFINE SCULPTURED SURFACE TO BE MACHINED
P1=POINT/0,0,20
P2=POINT/30,-5,26.5
P3=POINT/60,-5,26
P4=POINT/86,0,20
P5=POINT/-6,-30,15
P6=POINT/28,-25,22.75
P7=POINT/66,-25,22.5
P8=POINT/100,-30,15
SPLINE,P5,P6,P7,P8,     $
SPLINE,P9,P10,P11,P12
R1=POINT/30,-15,50
R2=POINT/70,-15,50
R3=POINT/0,0,0
R4=POINT/0,-30,0
C1=SCURV/CURSEG,R1,R2
C2=SCURV/CURSEG,R3,R4
DS1=SSURF/TRANSL,C1,CROSS,C2
TA=VECTOR/0,0,1
CUTTER/10,5
FROM/(STPT=POINT/50,-60,50)
SCON/INIT,ALL
SCON/DS,DS1,PARAM,0,1,0,1,ON,NORMAL
SCON/PS,TO,PS0,MINUS,0
SCON/AXIS,TA
SCON/STEPOV,0.5,5,0,0
SCON/FEED,100,200,50,3000
SMIL/ZIGZAG,DS,PARAM,0,0,TANSPL,PLUS,STEPOV,PLUS,0
```

NC and CNC

At present, Numerical Control NC (Numerical Control) and CNC (Computer Numerical Control) term carried the same meaning. By the name NC, it is assumed CNC Numerical Control, which controls the automation of machine tools with sophisticated computer control and memory capabilities and inherent all control capabilities of the old NC machines. The CNC machine tool uses servo motors and feedback technology to perform the multi-axis motions. The CNC program, lines of (ASCII) text, specify the movement, control functions, and coordinates of points prepared from CAD files (automatically using CAM software or manually). It is then inputted to the CNC memory manually, with a floppy disk or downloaded using serial/network connection. CNC has enough memory to store multiple programs. Further, the program can be recalled from memory executed, modified, and uploaded to storage on the computer or mainframe. The program remains in memory and can be reused and modified until it is explicitly deleted.

Table 2. Differences between NC and CNC machine tools

NC	CNC
Hard wired –Can' be changed	Computer controlled software based – easily changeable
Fixed Control logic for code, functions, commands	Microprocessor resident control logic - changeable
Control logic can be changed only with circuit boat replacement	All programs changeable
No memory and storage	Memory storage
Programs can't be created or modified on the machine. All programs are created externally on punched tape	Programs can be created or modified and stored on the machine. Program inputted via the network, serial communication, floppy disk (FD), or manually created.
Programs stored only on punched tape	Programs can be stored on the mainframe, server or CNC memory and uploaded trough directly connection or media (FD)
Each part need separate tape	Memory capacity store multiple programs indefinitely

Direct Numerical Control

The concept of Direct Numerical Control (DNC) to link a computer to the CNC machine CPU directly, see Figure 1.3. In the 1960s, one of the first companies to implement DNC was Cincinnati Milacron and General Electric. In the 1970's many DNC machines were built based on the concept of usage of one networked (shared) main computer to program, control, and execute machine operation on several NC machines. Although promising, the DNC systems were used only to transmit the program to CNC (NC) machines. Today is not very often used, although virtually all CNC machines are capable of DNC trough serial, network communication, storage cards, and devices.

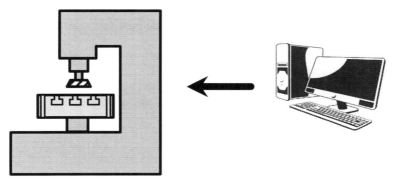

Figure 1.3 Direct Numerical Control

Distributed Numerical Control

With the development of NC machines and computer technology, new types of Computer Numerical Controlled (CNC) machines were built. They have a computer that was placed directly on the machine. At present, virtually all NC machines are CNC, and the new NC is used inter-exchangeable with CNC.

The CNC machine's capability to control and store programs made it possible to use for stand-alone operation. With the rapid advancement of computer technologies and networking and CNC machines, a new type of control, called Distributed Numerical Control, was developed, Figure 1.4. CNC and computers were connected through the network that provides not only program communication (downloading/uploading). Besides, they offer possibilities to control and automate the whole manufacturing system. Thus, DNC processed can provide functions such as machine and robot monitoring and control, scheduling and balancing of the automated lines, controlling the status data, and managing the whole process.

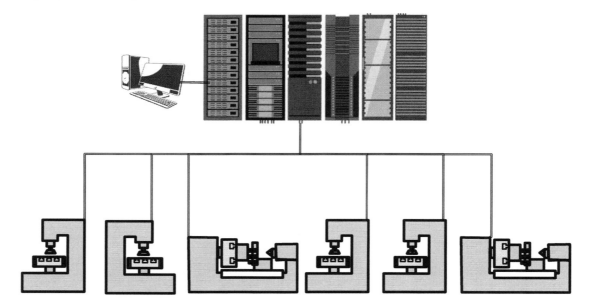

Figure 1.4 Distributed NC

CNC standards

Currently there are two widely recognized and accepted standards for language for computerized numerical control (CNC) programs. International Standard Organization (ISO) developed ISO 6383, and the Electronic Industries Alliance (EIA) developed EIA RS274D. Both standards are very similar and are followed by most of the countries of the word.

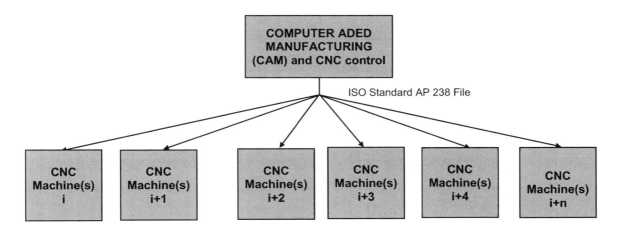

Figure 1.5 AP-238-STEP- Boeing

When those standards were developed (40-50 years ago), paper tape was the most common data medium, and CNC machines could process only simple commands. With the development of computer processing and graphics, capabilities 3 three-dimensional (3D) data is easily handled and processed. Still, NC programming stayed behind as the only one part of in CAD/CAM process that is not capable of 3D processing. A new Application protocol AP-238 as a part of the ISO STEP (STandard for the Exchange of Product model data) standard was developed to solve this problem, Figure 1.5. It allows the information to control a CNC machine and 3D data from CAD/CAM system to be associated and create the CNC control file (completely documented). An AP-238 file is carrying the product, manufacturing/machining, as well as processing information (including tolerance requirements), thus virtually encapsulating all the information needed for production.

Conversational programming of CNC

CNC controllers can be fitted with conversational (nonstandard) programming capabilities. The implementation is usually proprietary and depends on each CNC machine maker. Each machine may support both standards EIA/ISO (G and M codes) and conversational programming. The intent is to be easy for use on the machine floor by operators for a single part, manufacturing feature, or small batch production. Many of the CNC controller software can also convert the conversation program to standard standards EIA/ISO codes. Some of the most advanced conversation programming systems can be effortlessly programmed not only for simple parts but for parts with complicated features.

Programming CNC using CAD/CAM

Modern design and manufacturing processes have been applying the most advanced computer technology. The idea about utilizing the digital model workflow is to use the same CAD/CAM **3D data model** for both design and manufacturing processes, thus enabling easy updating for the data model for any changes during the production flow. 3D geometrical model from CAD is used in CAM to produce a cutter path, including cutter offsets, tool selection, cutting speed, and feed rate. Before transferring to the CNC machine, the cutter path program is verified for a specific machine for tool collision, shape, precision, and others. CAM software allows programming of complex parts and 3D shapes that are not possible with manual programming. Finally, at the inspection phase of the manufacturing process, the 3D geometrical model from CAD can be used to compare the data from the measured part from the machined part.

CNC machine and controller manufacturers

Leading controller manufacturers are Fanuc, Bendix, Bridgeport, Cincinnati Milacron, General Electric, Giddings, Haas, Lewis, Mitsubishi, Okuma, Siemens, and Yasnak. They are sometimes using their CNC controllers with a specialized machine processing unit (MPU) or enhanced personal computer processor units. Virtually almost all CNC manufacturers follow the ISO/EIA programming standards for most of the functions that make CNC programs portable between different machines, see Figure 1.6. On the other side, existing CAM software post processors (including their post processor CNC code generators) support creating programs for most of these controllers.

Figure 1.6 Different CNC machines

The major CNC tools manufacturing companies are Fanuc, Bendix, Bridgeport, Cincinnati Milacron, Emco, General Electric, Giddings, Haas, Lewis, Milltronics, Mitsubishi, Okuma, Siemens, and Yasnak. At present, there are thousands of CNC companies making CNC machines for milling, turning, grinding, water, laser and plasma cutting, punching and nibbling, electrical discharging machine – die sinking and wire types, and others.

References

[1] National Center for Manufacturing Sciences; The Next Generation Controller Part Programming Functional Specification (RS-274/NGC); Draft; NCMS; August 1994.

[2] Example of a regional milling program, retrieved on 04/04/2017
http://www.catapt.com/APTssman/apt2_8.htm#C8_4_2

Notes:

Chapter 2

Elements of CNC Machining

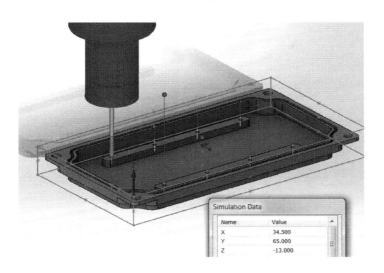

Figure 2.1 Point to point drilling operation

CNC system elements

CNC control system

There are two modes of CNC control system: Point to Point and Continuous path. Point to Point (PTP) is de-facto, a positioning system. The tool moves from a point to the next programmed point, then performs an operation such as drilling, boring, tapping, reaming, and threading, see Figures 2.1, 2.2, and 2.3.

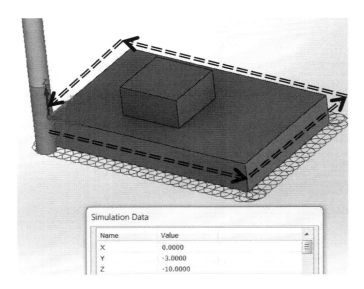

Figure 2.2 Point to point milling operation

15

The direction of travel can be along with one of the X and Y axis axes (Figure 2.1 and 2.2), or 45° degree angle path (Figure 2.3).

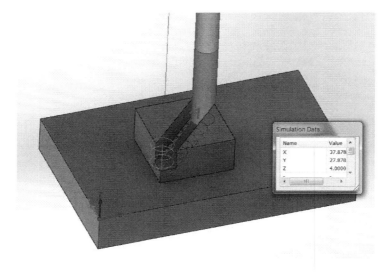

Figure 2.3 Point to point milling 45°

Typically, the PTP control system operates in the predefined steps. For example, as shown in Figure 2.1, the initial step is positioning to predefined holes' center coordinates; the next step is the actual machining along the Z axis with specific rotation speed, controlled feed rate, and depth of the cut. Subsequent steps are rapid retracting and repositioning to the next point, followed by repeating the machining, the final step is rapid retracting to a predefined final position.

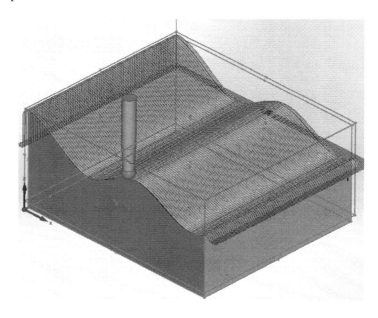

Figure 2.4. Continuous path contour 3D machining

The continuous path, also called the contouring system, is synchronized motion on the predefined path. The most common paths are linear and circular arc motion. The continuous path system involves simultaneously control on two, three, or more axes, see Figure 2.4. Depending on the capabilities to control the continuous path on several axes simultaneously, CNC machines can be classified on 2, 3, 4, 5, and 6 axis types. The simultaneous control of those axes is very complex and involves those machines' capabilities to control the motion of driving motors **independently** at various speeds. The contouring on a specific path is done by interpolation.

CNC Interpolation

Interpolation is the precise movements of the tool CNC on different axes while keeping the tool accurately on the desired programmed path.

Linear interpolation
Linear interpolation is a movement of the CNC tool on the linear path calculated by the CNC controller. For example, X2.0 commands the machine to move 2.0 only on the X-axis, Y3.0 controls the machine to move 3.0 only on one Y-axis. X4.0 Y4.0 the machine moves on X and Y with tiny single-axis increments simultaneously on each of the axes, thus creating a 45o line, see Figure 2.5. Similarly, a CNC machine can move precisely to any point defined in the program (e.g., next point X5.0 Y5.0). When linear interpolation command is issued, only the endpoint coordinates and feed rate (speed command) must be given; the CNC machines know its existing position so that it can calculate the path to the new point. Movement on each axis is controlled by CNC electronic device for up to five/six axis simultaneous (linear axes X, Y, and Z; rotation axes A, B, and C). The most common CNC machines can move in two or three axes simultaneously. Linear interpolation can be used to approximate different types of tool paths required in CNC machining: circular/arcs, spline curves, helical, parabolic, and others. Most of these approximations are calculated using a CAM system in advance, and resulting path programs are transferred to the CNC controller. This approach makes it possible to machine complex 3-D surfaces such as car body shape, ship hulls, aircraft wings, and others.

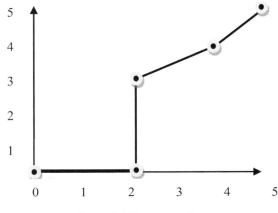

Figure 2.5 Point to point

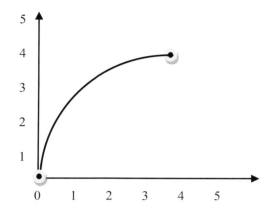

Figure 2.6 Circular Interpolation -continuous path

Circular interpolation
Circular interpolation is a movement of the CNC tool on the circular path calculated by the CNC controller. For example, G03 X3.0 Y.3 R1.5 commands the machine to move on an arc trajectory with a radius R1.5 on a clockwise direction (assuming starting point X10, Y0), see Figure 2.6. Movement on each axis is controlled by CNC electronic device for up to six-axis simultaneous (linear axis X, Y, and Z; rotation axis A, B, C). Typically, CNC machines support circular interpolation only on two axes simultaneously, for a circle/arc path lying on the same plane (XY, XZ, or YZ). Still, some more advanced CNC controllers can provide circular interpolation control in any direction or helical interpolation.

CNC Machine Control Unit

Machine Control Unit (MCU) controls all CNC functions such as data processing, input, output, and I/O (Input/Output) interface.

Typical MCU includes the following devices and systems:
1. CPU (Computer Control Unit)
2. Memory- RAM/ROM
3. Storage (secondary)
4. Communications
5. Spindle speed control
6. Servo drive control
7. System Bus –interconnect all the systems
8. Programmable machine controller (PMC) or sequencer

CPU
The Central Process Unit (CPU) controls MCU components using programming software loaded in the memory. CPU has three main sections: Control section that coordinates and controls all the functions executed by the CPU and access instructions from memory;

18

arithmetic-logical unit (ALU) that carry out all calculations and logical operations; and immediate access memory that store internally data from ALU and all instructions for immediate execution.

Memory
The memory includes Read-Only Memory (ROM) and Random Access Memory (RAM). ROM contains the operating system and its permanent memory. It remains in the storage even after the powers are switched off. NC programs are stored in RAM only for execution and are removed when the power is off.

Storage
Similar to the use on a personal desktop computer, a floppy disk or hard drive can contain all programs needed for NC machining. In the past, punched paper tapes were also used as a storage device. Modern CNC machines can store all the information, including control operation. Also, most of the new CNC machines can access program libraries as well as store programs on a remote server through a local area network. Flash memory or non-volatile (no power need to store information) computer memory (also called bubble memory) can also be used for storage functions.

Communications
Communications include interface I/O (input/output), cathode ray tube (CRT) or liquid crystal display (LCD) interface, RS232 serial communications, storage interface, network interface. Communication between CPU and CNC components is transported mainly through the system bus.

Spindle speed control
Most CNC machines can control the spindle speed is using a special speed function in the part program. The spindle speed control consists of a serial speed control circuit and a spindle speed feedback interface.

Servo drive control
Convert the machine control pulses to drive the axis control motors. Control from the CNC interface is done with the low power electrical signal that necessitates servo drive amplifiers that directly drive servo motors. The feedback system detects the actual position and sends the information back to the CPU, allowing precise regulation of the position and velocity.

Programmable machine controller (PMC)
The programmable machine controller provides the following functions: Automatic tool change, Coolant control, limit (end) switch interface, timer and counters, CNC input/output interface, and others.

CNC Software

The computer in CNC operates using three types of software:
    1 Operating system software,
    2. Machine interface software, and
    3. Application software.

The operating system software is the main program for the execution of CNC functions. There are few existing operation systems software vendors that provide it together with the control unit. The operating system software interprets the CNC part programs and generates the corresponding control signals to drive the machine tool axes

The machine interface software, provided by the machine builder, set the communication between the CPU and the machine tool to accomplish the CNC auxiliary functions.

The application software consists of the CNC part programs for machining applications and other functions at the end user-place.

CNC Machining process flow

Creating the CNC program is the final step of the CNC manufacturing process.
CNC manufacturing process = conventional manufacturing process.
Prior to start machining, a complete manual or computer-aided CNC manufacturing process needs to be developed.

Manual CNC process flow:
    1. Develop or obtain the part drawing.
    2. Decide which machine(s) will perform the operations needed to produce the part.
    3. Decide on the machining sequence and decide on cutter-path directions.
    4. Choose the tooling required and their organization on the machine.
    5. Do the required mathematics calculations for the program coordinates, including tolerance requirements.
    6. Calculate the spindle speeds, feed rates, and depth of the cut required for the tooling and part material.
    7. Write the CNC program.
    8. Prepare setup sheets and tool lists (these will also be used for manufacturing operators).
    9. Verify and edit the program, using a virtual machine simulator such as NC simulator, NC Viewer, NC plot, NCSIMUL, Inventor CAM Editor, etc.
    10. Transfer the program to the CNC machine.
    11. Verify and edit the program on the actual machine and make changes to it if necessary.
    12. Run the program and produce the final part.

Computer Aided CNC process flow:

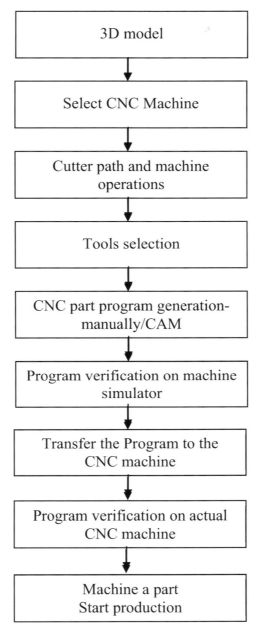

1. Develop or obtain the 3-D geometric model of the part-CAD
2. Decide which machining operations and cutter-path directions are required to produce the part (computer-assisted or engineering drawings and specifications).
3. Choose the tooling to be used (sometimes computer-assisted).
4. Run a CAM software program to generate the CNC part program, including the setup sheets and the list of the tools used.
5. Verify and edit the program, using virtual machine simulators such as Mastercam/SolidCAM/Inventor CAM/SurfCAM/Cimatron/CATIA/SiemensNX, etc.

6. Download the part program(s) to the appropriate machine(s) over the network (or storage media) and machine the prototype. (Sometimes multiple machines will be used to fabricate a part.)
7. Verify the program(s) on the actual machine(s) and edit them if necessary.
8. Run the program and produce the part. If in a production environment, the production process can begin.

Notes:

Notes:

Chapter 3

Fundamental Concepts of CNC Machining

Axis Motion

All existing CNC machines are based on the standard, so developed programs can be run on any machine since the motion control and coordinate points are defined the same way. A CNC program is based on the coordinate system that is common for any machine, independently of the axis motion implementation by different manufacturers. In some cases, the tool moves, in other the table moves or any combination of both. Yet, according to the CNC programming concepts and based on the standards, it is always assumed that the tool moves relative to the workpiece and the table. Thus, the programmer can create a tool path movement for tools regardless of how the machine works.

Coordinate system

The most common coordinate system used in CNC machining is the rectangular Cartesian coordinate system. CNC tool position is controlled related motion to this coordinate system along axes. Each linear axis is perpendicular (90° angle) to others. One can find the positive direction of an axis of the Cartesian coordinate system using the right-hand rule. The Cartesian coordinate system is also called the right-hand coordinate system, and both terms are used regularly.

Each axis's direction can be determined by holding the right hand with an extended thumb, forefinger, and middle finger perpendicular to each other. As shown in Figure 3.1, the thumb finger shows the positive X direction, forefinger the positive Y direction, and middle finger the positive Z direction. The machine spindle with the tool is always in the Z direction.

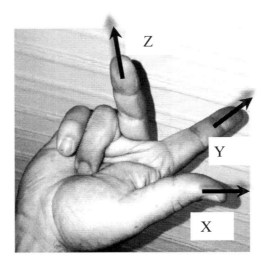

Figure 3.1. Using right-hand rule for determining X, Y, and Z coordinates

The most typical CNC milling machine setup is with the longest axis alongside X coordinate, thus defining the coordinate system can be easily defined by applying the

27

right-hand rule, Figure 3.2. In the case of CNC lathe, the Z is typically the longest axis passing through the spindle, as shown in Figure 3.3.

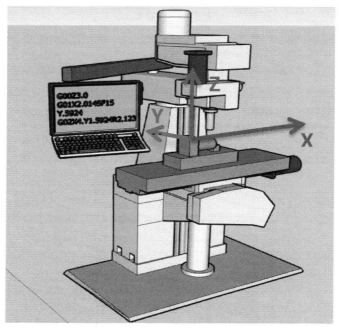

Figure 3.2   3-axis mill. X, Y, Z axis of movement. Z-axis through the spindle, X, Y perpendicular to Z and each other.

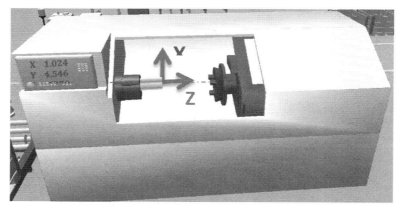

Figure 3.3 CNC lathe with Z and X-axis of movement. The primary Z-axis pass through the spindle and the secondary X- axes is perpendicular to the Z-axis.

Some machine has more than 2 or 3 moving axes. There are also 4 or 5 axis machines, where the 4 or both 4 and 5 axes are rotational, see Figure 3.4. The direction of the rotational axis can be defined by the right-hand rule for rotation, as shown in Figure 3.5. One can find the positive rotary motion axis by pointing the thumb in the direction of one of the linear axis (X, Y, Z), and the corresponding direction of the rotation axis (A, B, C) can be defined by following the curl of the rest of the fingers.

Figure 3.4 Five-axis CNC milling machine

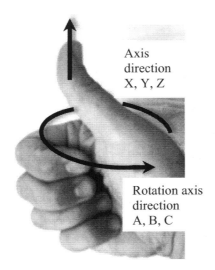

Figure 3.5 Right-hand rule for rotation motion about X, Y, and Z

CNC Milling machine fundamentals

As described before, all CNC milling machines use a three or more -axis coordinate system. The first axis X is typical along the longest moving side of the table. The second axis Y-axis is always perpendicular to the first and third axis. The third axis Z is the rotation spindle axis; it is always perpendicular to the first and second axis and can be vertical or horizontal, relative to the base of the machine.

Some CNC milling machines may have an additional axis with milling capabilities that allow complex surface machining; in such a case, one or more additional axis, linear or rotational, is used.

Figure 3.6 shows two axes –primary X and secondary Y, not shown is the Z-axis, which perpendicular to X, Y.

The XY coordinate plane is divided into four quadrants. The position of each point on the plane can be determined by the value and sign of the distance to each axis from the origin.

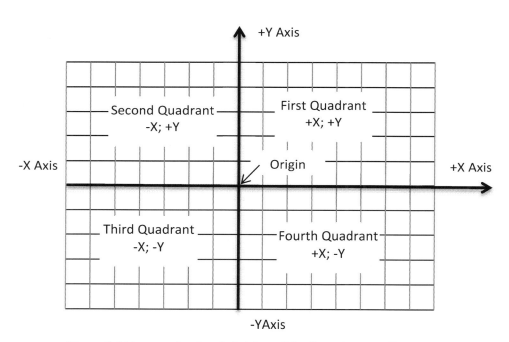

Figure 3.6 Four quadrants subdivision of the Cartesian coordinate system

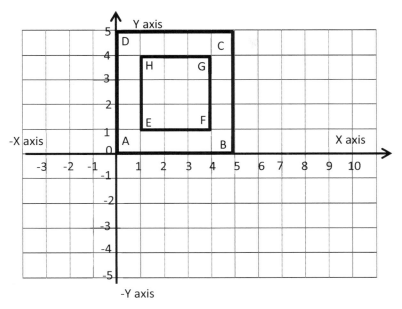

Figure 3.7 Part drawing on Cartesian coordinate system graph. The corner of two top sides
of the workpiece is usually set up to be at the origin of the coordinate system,
where the top the workpiece is set-up to be Z zero.

In other cases, for a rotational type of parts, the origin can be set up to be at the center of the radius of the workpiece. The coordinates of each point on profile and their sign the workpiece can be found using the four quadrants coordinate system. Please note that the X values can be positive or negative, see Figures 3.6, 3.7, and 3.8. For example, for the big square, as shown in Figure 3.7, if the starting point A of the profile of the workpiece is at the origin, it will be programmed as X0, Y0, then consecutive coordinate points are as follows: point B (X5 Y0), C (X5, Y5), and D (X0, Y5). For the small square E (X1, Y1) F (X4, Y1), G (X4, Y4), and H (X4, Y1).

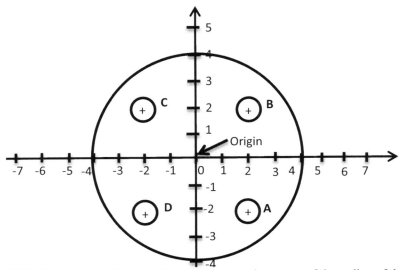

Figure 3.8 Workpiece set on the coordinate system on the center of the radius of the workpiece,
where the top the workpiece is set-up to be Z zero.

31

For example, for the circular shape part, as shown in Figure 3.8, the origin is X0, Y0, the first hole center A has coordinates X2, Y-2, the second hole center B (X2, Y2), the third hole center C(X-2, Y2), and the fourth hole center D(X-2, Y-2). The machining of the circle profile can be started and any desired point.

Programming with absolute and incremental coordinate

CNC programming allows using absolute or incremental coordinates, see Figure 3.9. The most common programming is using absolute values. For absolute programming, the coordinate of each point is measured directly from the origin. For incremental

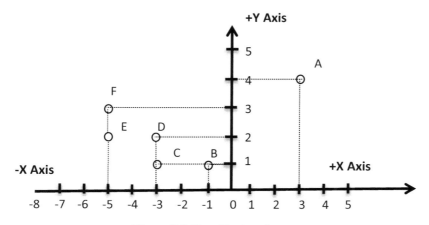

Figure 3.9 Coordinate values

programming, the coordinate of each point is measured from the previous point. CNC machine setting must be changed in the program for the absolute or incremental value. Absolute values are activated with the G90 code, and the incremental values are activated with the G91 code.

Programming with absolute coordinates

Programming a point on the profile of the workpiece is measured directly from the origin of the coordinate system. This programming is so-called absolute programming as the absolute values are measured directly from the origin of the coordinate system. Figure 3.10 shows an example of the absolute coordinate measured from the origin.

How to obtain absolute coordinate values:
For X, measure the distance from a point directly to coordinate axis X, for Y measure the distance from a point directly to coordinate axis Y. Also, the sign from each value depends on which quadrant is the measured point. Most users have no difficulties obtaining absolute coordinates for each point, since they had had previous experience from high school/college general classes in mathematics /physics, etc.
Let follow the example shown in Figure 3.10 to find the coordinate values for points A-F.

32

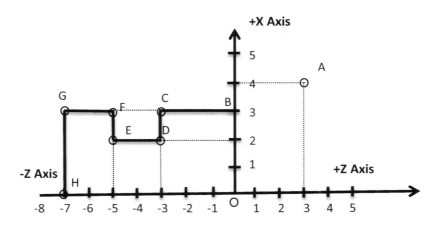

Figure 3.10 Programming with absolute values

The first point is always measured from the origin X0 Y0 of the coordinate system. Each X-axis point can be found directly below the measured point by traveling directly alongside the X-axis. Write down the X value. Next, go up directly to the measured point alongside the Y-axis and write down the Y value.

EXAMPLE: How to find coordinate values of point A
1. Start from the origin X0 Y0
2. Move to the right until you reach exactly bellow point A
3. Go up directly to the measured point A
Result: Values of the coordinates of point A are X3, Y4

EXAMPLE: How to find coordinate values of point B
1. Start from the origin Y0 X0
2. Move to the left until you reach exactly bellow point B
3. Go up directly to the measured point B
Result: Values of the coordinates of point B are X0, Y3

EXAMPLE: How to find coordinate values of point C
1. Start from the origin Y0 X0
2. Move to the left until you reach exactly bellow point C
3. Go up directly to the measured point C
Result: Values of the coordinates of point C are X-3, Y3

Similarly coordinates of points D, E and F are calculated.

Point D:

Result: Values of the coordinates of point D are X-3, Y2

Point E:

Result: Values of the coordinates of point E are X-5, Y2

Point F:

Result: Vvalues of the coordinates of point F are X-5, Y3

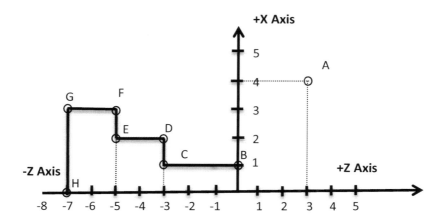

Figure 3.11 Programming with incremental values

Point G:

Result: Values of the coordinates of point G are X75, Y3

Point H:

Result: Values of the coordinates of point G are X-5, Y0

Programming with incremental coordinates

Programming of a point on the profile of the workpiece is measured directly from the previous point, see Figure 3.11. This method is not used very often and may create confusion for some users when calculating the values and values sign.

How to obtain incremental coordinate values:
The first point is measured from the origin of the coordinate system. Each subsequent point is measure from using as a reference to the previous point. In addition, the sign from each value depends not only on which quadrant is the measured point but in which direction you measure using the previous point as a reference. Most users have no difficulties obtaining absolute coordinates for each point but may have problems defining the incremental coordinates. One can verify the correctness of the calculated incremental value by finding the absolute values for each point first and then subtracting them from the previous reference point. Let follow the example shown in Figure 3.11 to find the incremental coordinate values for points A-F.

Each X and Y coordinate points can be found directly by measuring from the previous point. The first point is always measured from the origin X0, Y0 of the coordinate system.

34

EXAMPLE: How to find coordinate values of point A
1. Start from the origin X0 Z0
2. Move to the right until you reach exactly bellow point A
3. Go up directly to the measured point A
Result: Values of the coordinates of point A are X3, Y4

EXAMPLE: How to find coordinate values of point B
1. Start from point A
2. Move to the left until you reach exactly bellow the point B
3. Go down directly to the measured point B
Result: Values of the coordinates of point B are X-3, Y-3

EXAMPLE: How to find coordinate values of point C
1. Start from point B
2. Move to the left until you reach point C
3. Measured point C
Result: Values of the coordinates of point C are X-3, Y0

Similarly, coordinates of points D, E, and F are calculated.

Point D:

Result: Values of the coordinates of point D are X0, Y1

Point E:

Result: Values of the coordinates of point E are X-2, Y0

Point F:

Result: Values of the coordinates of point F are X0, Y1

Point G:

Result: Values of the coordinates of point G are X-2, Y0

Point H:

Result: Values of the coordinates of point H are X0, Y-3

Tools for Milling

Milling tools' size and specification are selected based on the size and shape of the features of the machined part. For each feature operation drilling, slotting, threading, pocket milling, thread, gear cutting, cutoff cutting specific toll is selected. Further tools for roughing and finished operation are selected based on performance and finish requirements. The material to be cut, the depth of the cut, chip load are other criteria for selecting the tool. Material, cutting speed and feed rate are specified by tool manufacturers to provide longer tool life and superior finish for a certain tool. Carbide tools can provide 5-10 times higher cutting speed than high-speed tools, have a longer tool life, and ca sustain high temperatures. The milling tool can be solid carbide type, solid high-speed steel or tool holders with replaceable carbide or ceramic inserts depending on the size and application.

Selecting the milling tool is based on the following parameters: the width and length of the cutting part, shape of the profile of the working part, tool material of the cutting part, number of the cutting edges (usually 2, 3, 4, 6, or 8), and the shape and type of the tool holder.

Drilling tools

Drilling tools are usually made from high-speed steel; for cutting harder materials, some tools are solid carbide type, and tools for large size cutting can be made with replaceable inserts. Drilling tools may have 2, 3, or 4 cutting lips. Two lips twisted flute drill is the most common type, while the 3 and 4 lips drills are used mostly to enlarge predrilled holes.

Figure 3.12 show an example of drilling tool specification according to ANSI/ASME B94.11M-1993.

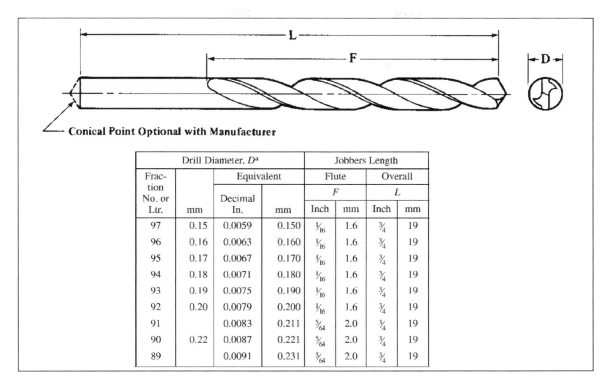

Drill Diameter, D^a				Jobbers Length			
Frac-tion No. or Ltr.		Equivalent		Flute		Overall	
				F		L	
	mm	Decimal In.	mm	Inch	mm	Inch	mm
97	0.15	0.0059	0.150	¹⁄₁₆	1.6	¾	19
96	0.16	0.0063	0.160	¹⁄₁₆	1.6	¾	19
95	0.17	0.0067	0.170	¹⁄₁₆	1.6	¾	19
94	0.18	0.0071	0.180	¹⁄₁₆	1.6	¾	19
93	0.19	0.0075	0.190	¹⁄₁₆	1.6	¾	19
92	0.20	0.0079	0.200	¹⁄₁₆	1.6	¾	19
91		0.0083	0.211	⁵⁄₆₄	2.0	¾	19
90	0.22	0.0087	0.221	⁵⁄₆₄	2.0	¾	19
89		0.0091	0.231	⁵⁄₆₄	2.0	¾	19

Figure 3.12. ANSI Straight Shank Twist Drills

Example of twisted and spot drilling tools and their parameter selections are shown in Figure 3.13 and 3.14

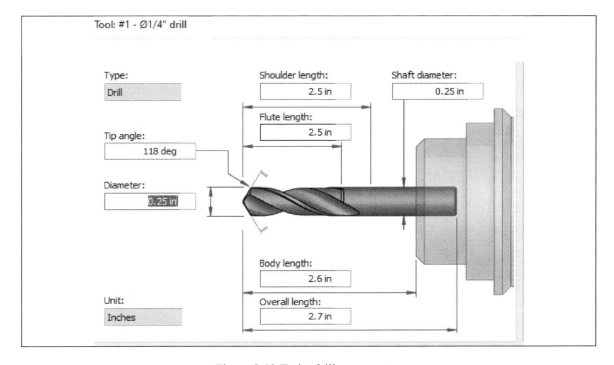

Figure 3.13 Twist drills parameters

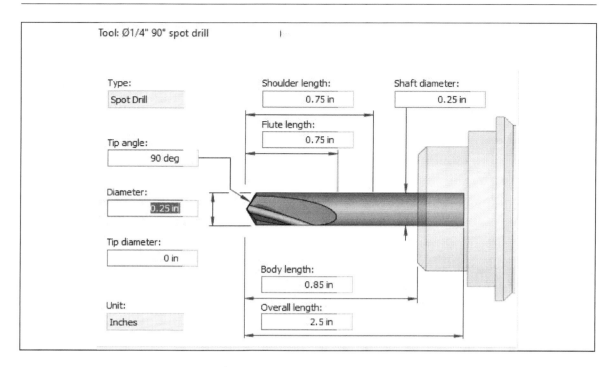

Figure 3.14 Spot drills parameters

Milling tools

There are many variations of shapes and size of milling tools that can be used for simple and complex shapes. The most widely used is the end milling tool, also called a flat end milling tool. Depends on the applications, different types of toll are uses, such as facing mill, bull nose mil, ball-end mill, shell mills, roughing mill.

Figure 3.15 show an example of two and four edge milling tools specification and Figure 3.16 show ANSI Roughing, Single-End End Mills High-Speed Steel according to American National Standard ANSI/ASME B94.19-1997.

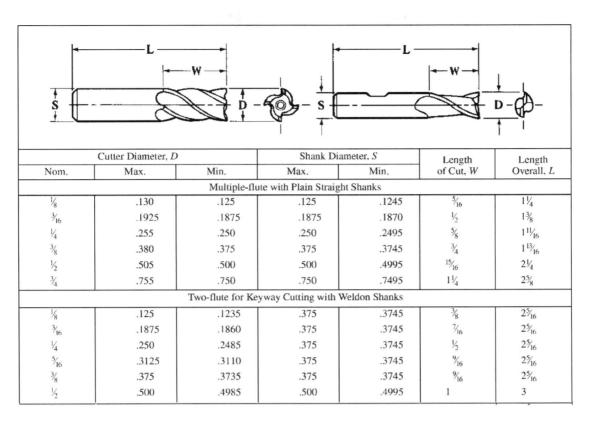

Cutter Diameter, *D*			Shank Diameter, *S*		Length of Cut, *W*	Length Overall, *L*
Nom.	Max.	Min.	Max.	Min.		
Multiple-flute with Plain Straight Shanks						
$\frac{1}{8}$	.130	.125	.125	.1245	$\frac{5}{16}$	$1\frac{1}{4}$
$\frac{3}{16}$	.1925	.1875	.1875	.1870	$\frac{1}{2}$	$1\frac{3}{8}$
$\frac{1}{4}$	.255	.250	.250	.2495	$\frac{5}{8}$	$1\frac{11}{16}$
$\frac{3}{8}$	.380	.375	.375	.3745	$\frac{3}{4}$	$1\frac{13}{16}$
$\frac{1}{2}$	.505	.500	.500	.4995	$\frac{15}{16}$	$2\frac{1}{4}$
$\frac{3}{4}$	.755	.750	.750	.7495	$1\frac{1}{4}$	$2\frac{5}{8}$
Two-flute for Keyway Cutting with Weldon Shanks						
$\frac{1}{8}$	.125	.1235	.375	.3745	$\frac{3}{8}$	$2\frac{5}{16}$
$\frac{3}{16}$	.1875	.1860	.375	.3745	$\frac{7}{16}$	$2\frac{5}{16}$
$\frac{1}{4}$	.250	.2485	.375	.3745	$\frac{1}{2}$	$2\frac{5}{16}$
$\frac{5}{16}$	.3125	.3110	.375	.3745	$\frac{9}{16}$	$2\frac{5}{16}$
$\frac{3}{8}$	.375	.3735	.375	.3745	$\frac{9}{16}$	$2\frac{5}{16}$
$\frac{1}{2}$	.500	.4985	.500	.4995	1	3

Figure 3.15 Multiple- and Two-Flute Single-End Helical End Mills

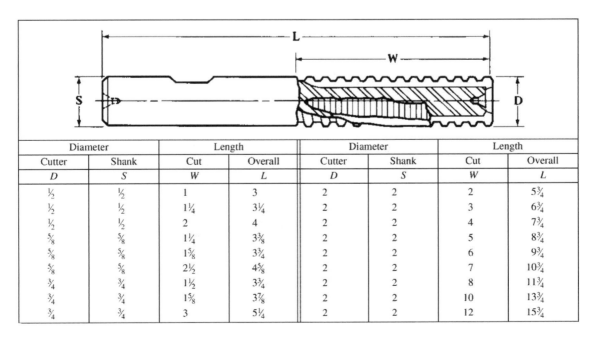

Diameter		Length		Diameter		Length	
Cutter	Shank	Cut	Overall	Cutter	Shank	Cut	Overall
D	*S*	*W*	*L*	*D*	*S*	*W*	*L*
$\frac{1}{2}$	$\frac{1}{2}$	1	3	2	2	2	$5\frac{3}{4}$
$\frac{1}{2}$	$\frac{1}{2}$	$1\frac{1}{4}$	$3\frac{1}{4}$	2	2	3	$6\frac{3}{4}$
$\frac{1}{2}$	$\frac{1}{2}$	2	4	2	2	4	$7\frac{3}{4}$
$\frac{5}{8}$	$\frac{5}{8}$	$1\frac{1}{4}$	$3\frac{3}{8}$	2	2	5	$8\frac{3}{4}$
$\frac{5}{8}$	$\frac{5}{8}$	$1\frac{5}{8}$	$3\frac{3}{4}$	2	2	6	$9\frac{3}{4}$
$\frac{5}{8}$	$\frac{5}{8}$	$2\frac{1}{2}$	$4\frac{5}{8}$	2	2	7	$10\frac{3}{4}$
$\frac{3}{4}$	$\frac{3}{4}$	$1\frac{1}{2}$	$3\frac{3}{4}$	2	2	8	$11\frac{3}{4}$
$\frac{3}{4}$	$\frac{3}{4}$	$1\frac{5}{8}$	$3\frac{7}{8}$	2	2	10	$13\frac{3}{4}$
$\frac{3}{4}$	$\frac{3}{4}$	3	$5\frac{1}{4}$	2	2	12	$15\frac{3}{4}$

Figure 3.16 Roughing, Single-End End Mills

Example of face mill, flat end mill, and ball end mill tools and their parameter selections are shown in Figures 3.17, 3.18, and 3.19.

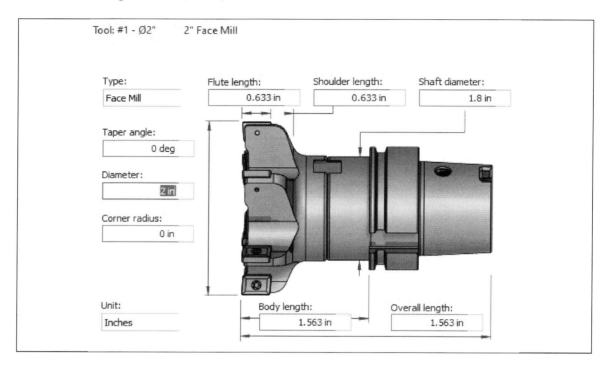

Figure 3.17 Face mill parameters

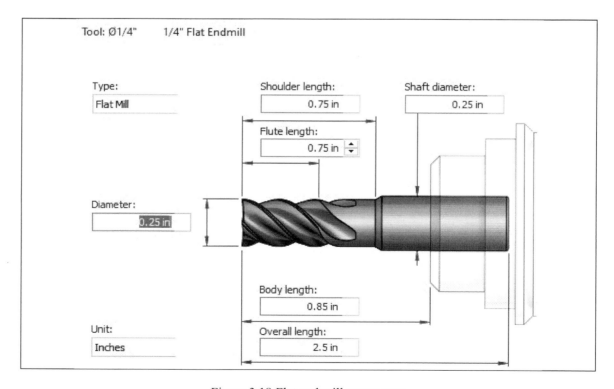

Figure 3.18 Flat end mill parameters

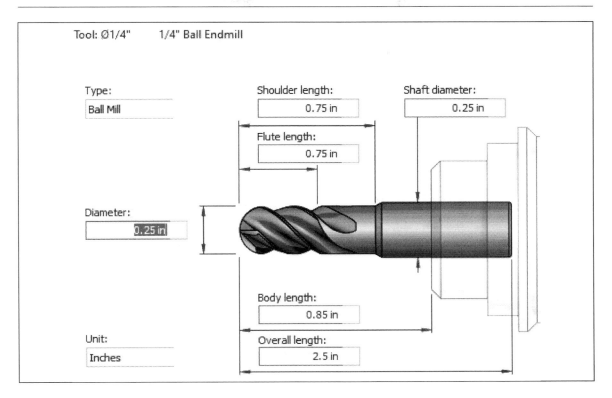

Figure 3.19 Ball endmill parameters

Other Tools

Tapping tools are used for making treads in holes. Depending on the speed, cycle, and tool holder, different types of tapping tools are used: Straight Flute Taps, Spiral Pointed Taps, Spiral Pointed Only Taps and Fast Spiral Fluted Taps. Some examples of taps, according to the ASME B94.9-1999 standard, are shown in Figure 3.20.

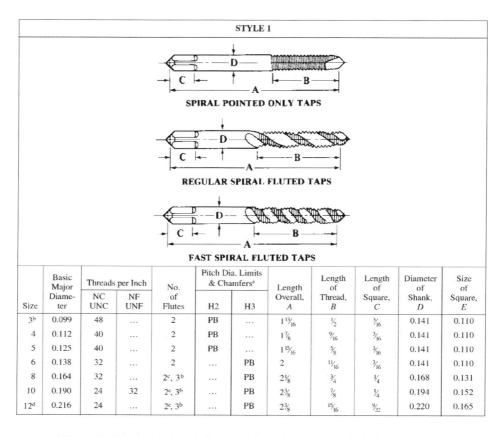

		STYLE 1									

SPIRAL POINTED ONLY TAPS

REGULAR SPIRAL FLUTED TAPS

FAST SPIRAL FLUTED TAPS

Size	Basic Major Diameter	Threads per Inch NC UNC	Threads per Inch NF UNF	No. of Flutes	Pitch Dia. Limits & Chamfers[a] H2	Pitch Dia. Limits & Chamfers[a] H3	Length Overall, A	Length of Thread, B	Length of Square, C	Diameter of Shank, D	Size of Square, E
3[b]	0.099	48	...	2	PB	...	$1\frac{13}{16}$	$\frac{1}{2}$	$\frac{3}{16}$	0.141	0.110
4	0.112	40	...	2	PB	...	$1\frac{7}{8}$	$\frac{9}{16}$	$\frac{3}{16}$	0.141	0.110
5	0.125	40	...	2	PB	...	$1\frac{15}{16}$	$\frac{5}{8}$	$\frac{3}{16}$	0.141	0.110
6	0.138	32	...	2	...	PB	2	$\frac{11}{16}$	$\frac{3}{16}$	0.141	0.110
8	0.164	32	...	2[c], 3[b]	...	PB	$2\frac{1}{8}$	$\frac{3}{4}$	$\frac{1}{4}$	0.168	0.131
10	0.190	24	32	2[c], 3[b]	...	PB	$2\frac{3}{8}$	$\frac{7}{8}$	$\frac{1}{4}$	0.194	0.152
12[d]	0.216	24	...	2[c], 3[b]	...	PB	$2\frac{3}{8}$	$\frac{15}{16}$	$\frac{9}{32}$	0.220	0.165

Figure 3.20 Spiral Pointed Only and Regular and Fast Spiral-Fluted Taps

Single Point Tools for Boring

Boring operations on CNC milling machines can also be performed using a single point tool. Since the boring tools have cylindrical shanks, a special tool milling shank needs to be used to hold them. Depends on the operation requirements, separate tools are needed for rough and finishing, drilling, boring, slotting and cutoff, and threads. It's common in the industry to use tools with indexable inserts. Tools with indexable inserts can be removed rotated, flipped, and reattached without changing the size and shape of the tool. Depends on the toolmaker tools produces are following one of the insert standards, the International Organization for Standardization (ISO) and America National Standard Institute (ANSI). Classification based on ISO 1832-2004 and ANSI B212.2.2002 include: Insert shape, relief angle, tolerances, insert type, size (IC), thickness, corner radius, left or right-hand insert, and cutting edge condition. ANSI B212.2.2002 specifies ten positions (Shape; Clearance; Tolerance class; Type; Size; Thickness; Cutting-point configuration; Edge preparation; Hand; Facet size) denoted by capital letter or number. Each one defines the specific characteristic of the insert as listed below:

1. Shape

Parallelogram	Diamond	Hexagon	Rectangle	Octagon	Pentagon	Round	Square	Triangle	Trigon
	H-120°								

42

A-85°	D-55°	K-120°	L-90°	O-135°	P-108°	R	S-90°	T-60°	W-80°
B-82°	E-75°								
K-55°	M-86°								
	V-35°								

Some common insert shapes are shown below:

2. Clearance-relief angles
A–3°; B–5°; C–7°; D–15°; E–20°; F–25°; G–30°; N–0°; and P–11°.

3. Tolerance class
There are 14 tolerance classes denoted by letters A, B, C, D, E, F, G, H, J, K, L, M, U, and N. For details, refer to the standard ANSI B212.2.2002 or Machinery's Handbook.

4. Type
There are 14 types of inserts with different designs (holes, countersinks, special features, and rakes) denoted by letters A, B, C, D, F, G, H, J, M, N, Q, R, T, U, W, and X. For details refer to the standard ANSI B212.2.2002 or Machinery's Handbook.

5. Size
The size defines the inscribed circle (IC) for inserts with Round, Square, Triangle, Trigon, Pentagon, Hexagon, Octagon, and Diamond. One digit for 1/8" (e.g. 1 – 1/8"; 2 – 1/4", and so on), and two-digits when isn't a whole number (e.g. 1.2 – 5/32"; 1.5 – 3/16" and so on). For details, refer to the standard ANSI B212.2.2002 or Machinery's Handbook.

6. Thickness
One or two digit numbers showing the thickness of the inserts in 1/16". For details, refer to the standard ANSI B212.2.2002 or Machinery's Handbook.

7. Cutting-point configuration
The cutting point configuration can have a radius or facet shape. For details, refer to the standard ANSI B212.2.2002 or Machinery's Handbook.

8. Edge preparation
The edge preparation indicated by the capital letter (A, B, C, E, F, J, K, P, S, and T) define the edge treatment and surface finish. For details, refer to the standard ANSI B212.2.2002 or Machinery's Handbook.

9. Hand
The hand define type of the tool R-Right hand; L-Left hand; and N-Neutral

10. Facet size

The Facet size is used if there is a letter for Cutting-point configuration in the seventh position. It number represent 1/64". For details, refer to the standard ANSI B212.2.2002 or Machinery's Handbook.

For example, a tool insert with the notation:

1	2	3	4	5	6	7	8	9	10
T	N	M	G	5	4	3			A

Represents a tool with the following parameters:

1-T- Shape is Triangle–60°; 2-N-Relieve angle is 0°; 3-M-Tolerances are: Inscribe circle -0.002-0,004; Thickness-0.005; 4-G-Type is Chip grove both surface with a hole; 5-5-Size-IC size 5 is 5/8"; 6-4-Thickness- is 1/4"; 7-3- Cutting-point configuration-is 3/64". Position 8, 9, and 10 are used when required.

Note: When using metric boring bar tools, you can refer to ISO standard: ISO 6261:2011 Boring bars (tool holders with cylindrical shank) for indexable inserts — Designation.

Notes:

Notes:

Notes:

Chapter 4

CNC

Milling Programming

(G and M code)

Letter addresses used in CNC milling

Letter addresses or words used in CNC milling are followed by a variable value used in programming with G and M codes each state or movement. The most common addresses used in CNC turning are listed below. Refer to the operator and program manual for a specific machine for exact words and their usage.

Letter	Description
A	A axis of machine
B	B axis of machine
C	C axis of machine
D	Depth of cut
	Dwell time
	Tool radius compensation number
F	Feed rate
G	Preparatory function
I	X axis center (incremental) for arcs
J	Y axis center (incremental) for arcs
K	Z axis center (incremental) for arcs
M	Miscellaneous function
N	Block number
P	Start block canned cycles
	Dwell time in canned cycles and with G4
Q	End block canned cycles
R	Arc radius or canned cycle plane
S	Spindle speed
T	Tool selection
U	U stock in X direction
	X incremental coordinate
V	V stock in Y direction
	Y incremental coordinate
V	W stock in Z direction
	Z incremental coordinate
X	X coordinate
Y	Y coordinate
Z	Z coordinate

G and M commands used in CNC milling

G and M commands used in CNC turning are followed by a variable value used in programming. The most common G and M code command used in CNC turning are listed below. Refer to operator and program manuals for a specific machine for the exact command and their usage.

Code	Parameters	Description	
MOTION	**(X Y Z A B C U V W apply to all motions)**		
G00		Rapid Move	Modal
G01		Linear Interpolation	Modal
G02, G2	I J K or R, P	Circular Interpolation CW	Modal
G03, G3	I J K or R, P	Circular Interpolation CCW	Modal
G04	P	Dwell	
G28	X Y Z	Automatic Zero Return	
G29	X Y Z	Return from Zero Return Position	
CANNED CYCLES	**(X Y Z or U V W apply to canned cycles, depending on active plane)**		
G73	R L Q	Drilling Cycle with chip breaking	Modal
G76	P Z I J R K Q H L E	Threading Cycle	Modal
G81	R L (P)	Drilling Cycle	Modal
G82	R L (P)	Spot/Counter Boring Cycle	Modal
G83	R L Q	Peck Drilling Cycle	Modal
G84	R L (P)	Taping Cycle	Modal
G80		Cancel Canned Cycle	Modal
DISTANCE MODE			
G90		Absolute Programming	Modal
G91		Incremental Programming	Modal
FEED RATE MODE			
G98		Canned Cycle Return Level	Modal
G99		Canned Cycle Return Level (position)	Modal
SPINDLE CONTROL			
M03	S	Spindle Rotation Control - CW	Modal
M04	S	Spindle Rotation Control - CCW	Modal
M05		Stop Spindle	Modal
COOLANT			
M08		Coolant Start	Modal
M09		Coolant off	Modal
STOPPING			
M00		Program Pause	

Code	Parameters	Description	
M01		Optional Program Pause	
M02		Program End	
M30		Program End, return to the beginning	
UNITS			
G20		Inch Units	Modal
G21		MM Units	Modal
CUTTER RADIUS COMPENSATION			
G40		Compensation Off	Modal
G41	D	Cutter Compensation Left	Modal
G42	D	Cutter Compensation Right	Modal
RETURN MODE IN CANNED CYCLES			
G98		Canned Cycle Return Level	Modal
OTHER MODAL CODES			
F		Set Feed Rate	Modal
S		Set Spindle Speed	Modal
T		Select Tool	Modal
G54-G59.3		Select Coordinate System	Modal
NON-MODAL CODES			
	T	Tool Change	
G28		Go/Set Predefined Position	
M101 - M199	P Q	User Defined Commands	
COMMENTS & MESSAGES			
/		Block skip	
(...)		Comments	
CNC program flow control			
O xxxx		Subroutines call (xxxx subroutine program #)	

G00 Rapid Linear Motion

Format structure: G00X__Y__Z__ (G00X__ / G00Y__ /G00Z__ / G0X__Y__Z__)

Rapid position the tool to the position specified by the cordites after the command. The rate of movement is the fastest possible for a certain machine. Depending on the machine design, it may move directly on the straight line to the designated point, see Figure 4.1. On some machines, the tool moves simultaneously on both axis (at 45° degree angle) and then straight line on the axis direction with remaining value, as shown in Figure 4.2. Therefore, it is good practice to move only on a single axis or a plane at one time, thus avoiding the possibility of tool collisions with the table or workpiece during the rapid movements. Rapid movement to approach point on the workpiece shall be avoided when possible; instead, a feed rate motion on the desired trajectory shall be used.

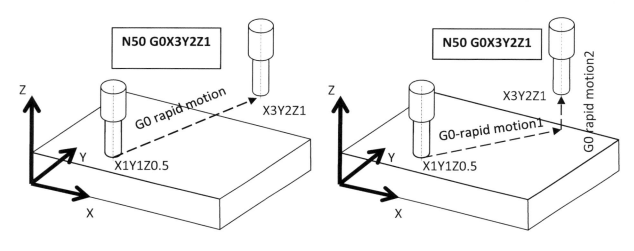

Figure 4.1 Rapid motion   Figure 4.2 Rapid motion 1 at 45°degree

G00 Command Example:

N50 G00 X0.125 Y0.25   Rapid move from present coordinates position to X0.125 Y0.25

*Note: **G00** (modal) use is **optional** and not need to be specified again in the next block **N60**.*

G01 Linear Interpolation

Format structure: G01X__ Y__ Z__ F__ (G01X__/G01Z__ / G1X__Z__ / G1X__ / G1Z__)

Linear interpolation G01 command executes the movement on a straight line with a specified constant feed rate (inch/min or mm/min). Cutting of the tool can move simultaneously on all axes X, Y, and Z with synchronized feed rate, it also can move along one or two of the axes X, Y, or Z, see Figure 4.3.

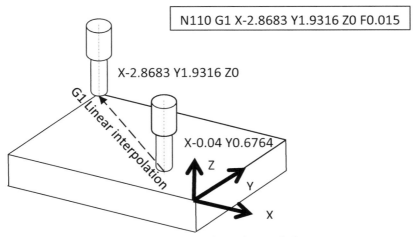

Figure 4.3 Linear interpolation

G01 Command Example:

N110 G01 X-2.8683 Y1.9316 Z0 F15   Linear interpolation to X-2.8683 Y1.9316 Z0, feed rate 15 inch/min

G02 Circular Interpolation Clockwise (CW)

Format structure: G02X__Y__ I__K_ F__ (*or* G2X__Z__ I__K__ F__ *or* G2Y__Z__I__K_ F_)

G02X__Y__ R__ F__ (or G2X__Z__ R__ F__ or G2Y__Z__ R__ F__)

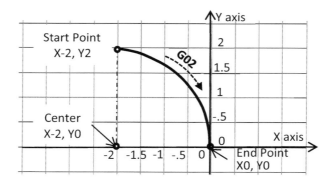

Figure 4.4 G02 Circular Interpolation Clockwise (CW) parameters

Circular interpolation clockwise motion G02 command executes the movement on the circular trajectory with the specified constant feed rate. Cutting of the tool moves simultaneously following circular arc on both axes X and Y (or XZ, or YZ) with the specified radius keeping feed rate synchronized. For calculating the tool motion trajectory on a circular arc, several parameters need to be explicitly defined, see Figure 4.4:

1. Endpoint coordinate values X and Y
2. The circular arc radius R or the incremental distance I (in X direction) and J (in Y direction) from the starting point to the center of the arc. Depending on the CNC machine configuration, R values usage may be limited to 90° or 180° degrees of rotation. There is no limitation if I and J are used. Note that I and J are vectors; therefore, they have sign +/- defined by the difference in coordinate values between the arc starting point and the center of the arc.
3. Feed rate (inch/min or mm/min)

The G2 command is modal; therefore, there is no need to be specified again if the current mode is G2.

G02 Command Example:

N140 G02 X-0.0537 I-0.3437 F14   90° CW Circular interpolation-**X0.0537 I-0.3437**, feed rate **14,** radius 0.**5**

G02 Example using radius:

N140 G2 X-0.0537 R0.5 F14   90° CW Circular interpolation-**X0.0537 I-0.3437**, feed rate **14,** radius 0.**5**

54

G03 Circular Interpolation Counter Clockwise (CCW)

Format structure: G03X__Y__ I__K__F__ *(or* G3X__Z__ I__K__ F__ *or* G3Y__Z__I__K__F__)

G03X__Y__ R__ F__ (or G3X__Z__ R__ F__ or G3Y__Z__ R__ F__)

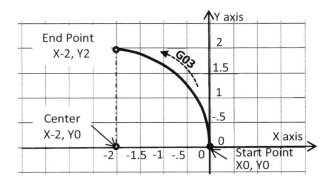

Figure 4.5 G03 Circular Interpolation Counter Clockwise (CCW) parameters

Circular interpolation counter clockwise motion G03 command executes the movement on the circular trajectory with the specified constant feed rate. Cutting of the tool moves simultaneously following circular arc on both axes X and Y (or XZ, or YZ) with the specified radius keeping feed rate synchronized. For calculating the tool motion trajectory on a circular arc, several parameters need to be explicitly defined, see Figure 4.5:

1. Endpoint coordinate values X and Y
2. The circular arc radius R or the incremental distance I (in X direction) and J (in Y direction) from the starting point to the center of the arc. Depending on the CNC machine configuration, R values usage may be limited to 90° or 180° degrees of rotation. There is no limitation if I and J are used. Note that I and J are vectors; therefore, they have sign +/- defined by the difference in coordinate values between the arc starting point and the center of the arc.
3. Feed rate (inch/min or mm/min)

The G03 command is modal; therefore, there is no need to be specified again if the current mode is G03.

G03 Command Example:

N100 G03 X0.2741 Y0.6474 I0.1875 F0.018   CCW Circular interpolation X0.2741 Y0.6474
I0.1875, feed rate F.018

G03 Example using radius:

N100 G03 X0.2741 Y0.6474 R0.25 F18   CCW Circular interpolation X0.2741 Y0.6474 I0.1875,
feed rate F.018

G04 Dwell

Format structure: G04 P__   (G4 P__)

   P__ seconds to dwell. P is a floating number.

Dwell G04 executes awaiting command (non modal) in seconds defined by the amount of time specified after P__. It is frequently used with drilling operations to clear the drilled hole's bottom surface, contra bore, or bottom of a surface. During the dwell, the feed rate is paused on all axes, while the spindle rotation, coolant, and other operations remain functional, see Figure 4.6. Since the P number is floating, it can be defined in seconds and a fraction of a second. Note that dwell command is for pause for a short time it is not modal and needs to be defined whenever it is executed. For longer pause of the program, M00 or M01 shall be used instead.

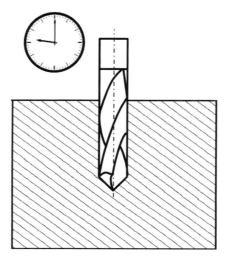

Figure 4.6 G04 Dwell waiting command

G04 Command Example:

N80 G4 P1.05   **Dwell for 1.05 seconds**

The example above shows the feed rate of tool movements stopped for 1.05 seconds.

G17 XY plane selection

Format structure: N_ G17

G17 command set the programming system to the XY plane. It is not a single plane, but any plane parallel to the XY axis. G17 - XY plane set is the default setting on CNC at startup and needs to be activated only when another plane was selected in one of the previous operations. It is used with circular interpolation, including cutter compensation, when applied. Rapid movement and linear interpolation are not affected, and they still work in any direction independently of plane selection command. G17 can also be activated together with other G codes, for example:

G17 Command Example:

N20 G17   **G17 XY plane selection**

G18 XZ plane selection

Format structure: G18

G18 command set the programming system to the XZ plane. It is not a single plane, but any plane parallel to the XZ axis. It is used with circular interpolation, including cutter compensation, when applied. Rapid movement and linear interpolation are not affected, and they still work in any direction independently of plane selection command.

G18 Command Example:

N100 **G18** G03 X-2.8249 Z-1.196 I-1.0 F20   **G18 –YZ PLANE SELECTION**, CCW Circular Interpolation X-2.8249 Z-1.1963 I-1.0, feed rate F20

G19 YZ plane selection

Format structure: G19

G19 command set the programming system to the YZ plane. It is not a single plane, but any plane parallel to the YZ axis. It is used with circular interpolation, including cutter compensation, when applied. Rapid movement and linear interpolation are not affected, and they still work in any direction independently of plane selection command.

G19 Command Example:

N80 **G19** G02 Y1.9729 Z-0.0554 J-0.025   **G19- YZ plane selection**, CW Circular interpolation Y1.9729 Z-0.0554 J-0.025, feed rate F10

G20 Inch Units

Format structure: G20

G20 command sets the programming in inch unit. All coordinate values (X, Y, Z) are set up in inches and feed rates in inch per revolution or inch per minute immediately after issuing the G20 command. The inch unit command G20 is modal, therefore it not need to be specified again if the current mode is G20. It is practical to set up the G20 at the beginning of the program and not change units later in the program.

G20 command example:

N10 G20 G90   **Inch Units, Absolute programming**

G21 Millimeter Units

Format structure: G21

G21 command sets the programming in millimeters unit. All coordinate values (X, Y, Z) are set up in millimeters and feed rates in millimeters per revolution or millimeters per minute immediately after issuing the G21 command. The millimeter unit command G21 is modal, therefore it not need to be specified again if the current mode is G21. It is practical to set up the G21 at the beginning of the program and not change units later in the program. Feed rates are specified in mm per rotation, or mm per minute.

G21 command example:

N20 G21   **Millimeters Units**

G28 Return to Home Position

Format structure: G28 or G28X__Y__Z__

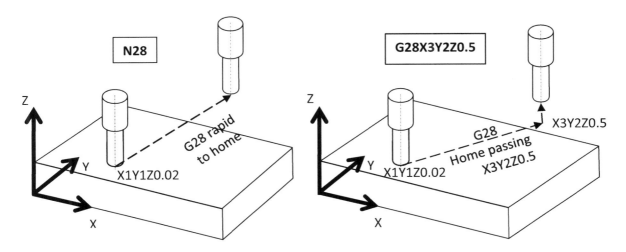

Figure 4.7 G28 rapid move direct to home position   Figure 4.8 G28 rapid move to home position via intermediate point

G28 command returns the machine to the home position with rapid speed (G00). If there are no coordinate values specified, the machine moves rapidly to home (also called machine zero) position, see Figure 4.7. If coordinate values X and or Y and or Z are specified, the machine moves rapidly to home passing through this coordinate position, see Figure 4.8. G28 is used when there are obstacle features on the way of the movement of the tool to the home position; therefore, it is necessary in such a case to define an intermediate position for the tool to pass to avoid collision on workpiece features.

G28 command example:

N130 G28 X-2.5 Y1.2   **Rapid Return to Home Position via X-2.5 Y1.2**

G29 Return from Home Position

Format structure: G29 or G29 X_Y_Z_

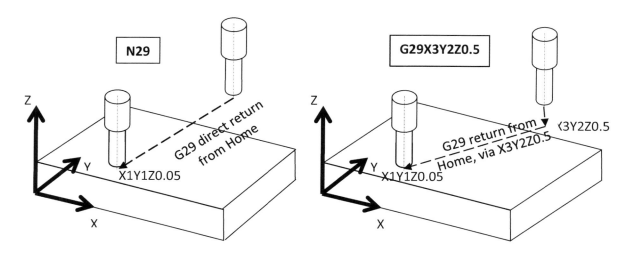

Figure 4.9 G29 direct return from home position

Figure 4.10 G29 return from position via intermediate point

G29 command is used immediately to return the machine with rapid speed (G00) to the starting point of G28 before going to the home position, see Figure 4.9. If there are no coordinate values specified, the machine moves rapidly to the start point. If coordinate values X and or Y and or Z are specified, the machine returns rapidly to the starting point of G28 passing through this coordinates position, see Figure 4.10. G29 is usually used when there are obstacle features on the way of the movement of the tool when returning from the home position, therefore, it is necessary in such a case to define an intermediate position for the tool to pass to avoid collision of the tool on workpiece features.

G29 command example:

N200 G29 X-2.59 Y1.165   **Return from Home Position via X-2.59 Y1.165**

G41 Tool Radius Compensation Left

Format structure: G41_D_

Tool compensation, also called cutter offset, is used to compensate for the tool radius/diameter (Figures 4.11 and 4.12), so the tool path follows exactly the profile from part drawing. It is also applied to compensate for the tool wear. Writing a program for the CNC tool center to follow the desired tool path without considering tool size at the time of program creation. It also allows for flexibility of selection of the tool size by the operator at the machine site if the curtain tool is not available. Further, it can be used to create a rough path without extra calculations for a new path by specifying a smaller tool diameter and then finishing the machining with actual tool size.

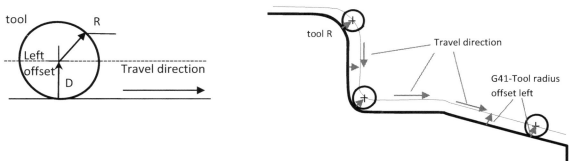

Figure 4.11 Tool radius compensation is equal to the tool radius (0.5diamer)

Figure 4.12 Part profile with tool radius compensation on the left

The reference point used for the tool center setting is different from the tool's profile with radius R (diameter 2R), as shown in Figure 4.11. The tool radius cutter compensation (also called offset) left, relative to the travel direction, is used, as shown in Figure 4.12.

Using radius compensation allow programming of the tool path, with actual coordinates without need to recalculate coordinates. The offset value is kept inside the CNC controller in Tool Offset Registry Table. The value is assigned during the machine set up. This value is called in the program when the tool is called via the tool set up reference number (or D number). When the offset is invoked, this causes the value stored in the setup table to be added or subtracted (multiplied with proper ratio), to the tool movement coordinates. Tool radius compensation G41 in the program must be followed by actual movement rapid G00 or linear interpolation G01 motion with enough travel distance, more than the tool radius. Tool compensation offset must be canceled with G40 after completion of the tool path to avoid influence the offset value on the next tools or operations. For example, T6 call tool number 6 with its offset number D, which calls the actual value of the offset from Offset Registry Table. Note that the number D is only a reference to the offset number from the machine Offset table of the tool size, not the actual size of the tool. The operator and CNC programmer must match the reference numbers from the program and offset table.

G41 command example:

N100 G41 G01 X0.   **LEFT side Tool radius compensation**, Linear interpolation to X0

| **G42 Tool Radius Compensation Right** |

Format structure: G42_D_

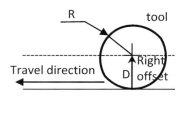

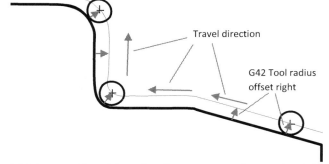

Figure 4.13 Tool radius compensation

Figure 4.14 Part profile with tool radius compensation on the right

The reference point for the tool center setting is different from the tool's profile with radius R (diameter 2R), as shown in Figure 4.13. The tool radius cutter compensation (also called offset) right, relative to the direction of the travel, is used as shown in Figure 4.14. Using the radius compensation allow programming of the tool path, with actual coordinates without need to recalculate coordinates. The offset value is kept inside the CNC controller in Tool Offset Registry Table. The value is assigned during the machine set up. This value is called in the program when the tool is called via the tool set up a reference number (or D number). When the offset is invoked, this causes the value stored in the setup table to be added or subtracted (multiplied with proper ratio), to the tool movement coordinates. Tool radius compensation G42 in the program must be followed by actual movement rapid G00 or linear interpolation G01 motion with enough travel distance, more than the tool radius. Tool compensation offset must be canceled with G40 after completion of the tool path to avoid influence the offset value on the next tools or operations. For example, T7 call tool number 7, with its offset number D, calls the actual value of the offset from Offset Registry Table. Note that the number D only references the offset number from the machine Offset table of the tool size, not the actual size of the tool. The operator and CNC programmer must match the reference numbers from the program and offset table.

G42 command example:

N100 G42 G01 X1.6091 Y0.6074   **RIGHT side Tool radius compensation, Linear interpolation to X1.6091 Y0.6074**

G40 Tool Radius Compensation Cancel

Format structure: G40_

G40 Tool radius compensation cancel is used to remove radius compensation invoked with tool nose radius compensation G41-left offset or G42-right offset, see Figures 4.15. and 4.16. Since the tool radius compensation is modal, it needs to be canceled to avoid confusion. It is also routine G40 to be placed at the beginning of the program to remove any remaining radius compensations. Note that Return to Home Position G28 command does not cancel offset; therefore, G40 must be used before invoking G28 or any tool changes.

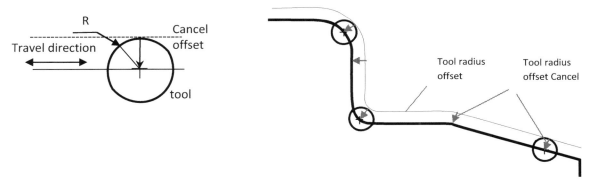

Figure 4.15 Tool nose radius compensation cancel   Figure 4.16 Profile errors for a tool without radius nose compensation

G40 command example:

N350 G40 G01 X-0.25   **Cancel Radius Compensation, Linear interpolation X-0.25**

G43/G44 Tool Length Compensation

Format structure: G43_H_(G44_H)

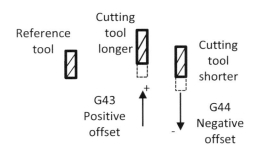

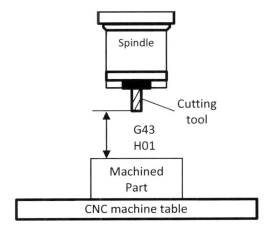

Figure 4.17 Tool length compensation G43 and G44   Figure 4.18 Tool length compensation G43 from the machined part

63

The G43 command compensates for tool length in the positive direction, and G44 command compensates for tool length in the negative direction, as shown in Figure 4.17. The tool length compensation (also called length offset) relative to the machined part is used, as shown in Figure 4.18. Using length compensation allows programming of the tool path, with actual coordinates without need to recalculate coordinates based on each tool's length. The H number (usually sale as the tool member) specified the length offset is kept inside the CNC controller in Tool Offset Registry Table. The value is assigned during the machine set up. This value is called in the program when the tool is called via the tool set up reference number (and H number). When the offset command is invoked, the value stored in the setup table is added or subtracted (multiplied with proper ratio) to the tool's position. From the operator/programmer viewpoint, this offset simplifies the programming and operation to represent machining as using the same tool. Tool compensation offset must be canceled with G49 after completion of the tool path to avoid influence the offset value on the next tools or operations. For example, T9 call tool number 9 with its offset number H09, which calls the actual value of the offset from Offset Registry Table. Note that the number H is only referencing the offset number from the machine Offset table of the tool size, not the actual length of the tool. The CNC operator and programmer must match the reference numbers from the program and offset table.

G43 command example:

N20 T1 G43 H01 M06   **Tool change Tool#1, length offset #01**

G49 Tool Length Compensation Cancel

Format structure: G49_

G49 Tool length compensation cancel is used to remove length compensation invoked with G43-positive length offset or G44-negative length offset, see Figures 4.19 and 4.20. Since tool compensation is modal, it needs to be canceled to avoid confusion. It is also routine G49 to be placed at the beginning of the program to remove any remaining radius compensations. Note that Return to Home Position G28 command does not cancel offset; therefore, G49 must be used before invoking G28 or any tool changes.

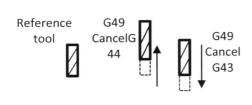 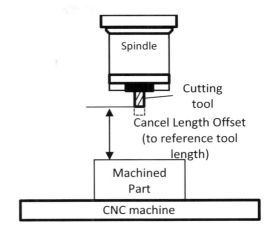

Figure 4.19 Tool length compensation cancel   Figure 4.20 Tool length compensation cancel from the machined part

G49 command example:

N150 G49   **Cutter compensation length cancel**

G54-G59 Select Work Coordinate System

Format structure: G54_(G55_, G56_, G57_, G58_, G59_)

There are six G-codes (#1-G54, #2-G55, #3-G56, #4-G57, #5-G58, and #6-G59) that can be used to assign workpiece coordinates. They can be used to multi-feature coordinate set up for one or more workpieces, see Figure 4.21. In some CNC machines, coordinate can be optionally extended, for example, up to 48 more using command and P number, G51.1P1 to G51.P48.

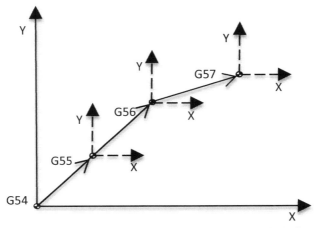

Figure 4.21 G54-59 Commands Example and tool motion

G54-59 command example:

N40 G55 X0.5 Y0.5   **Set the coordinate system #1 G55 at position X0.5 Y0.5**

G73 High Speed Deep Hole Drilling Cycle

Format structure: $G73\ X\_\ Y\_\ Z\_\ R\_\ Q\_\ K\_\ F\_$

G73 High Speed Deep hole drilling cycle includes peck drilling and retracting on each hole; it is used for deep drill multiple holes at specific locations listed within the cycle by coordinates after the cycle, see Figure 4.22. In the High Speed Deep drilling cycle G73, X defines coordinate of the first hole in the X-axis, Y defines the coordinate of the first hole in the Y-axis, Z defines the full depth of the hole (the tool will travel to Z depth with the federate F), R defines the position of the retract distance, Q pecking defines the incremental drilling distance on individual pecks (depth with the federate F), and F defines the feed rate for hole machining. After each peck drilling movement, the tool moves back rapidly to predefine distance and repeats this pecking cycle until it reaches the full depth Z of the hole. The pecking drilling cycle allows the removal of chips from the hole after each peck; this permits machining of deep holes without breaking the tool. Since the peck retread distance is shorter than a complete retreat to retract pane, as in G83, the G73 cycle is faster. G73 cycle defines the location of the first hole; the machines will continue to drill holes according to the coordinates specified bellow G73 until the cycle is canceled with the G80 cycle cancel command. All of the holes in the cycle are machining with the feed rate F and pecking settings specified in the G73 cycle block.

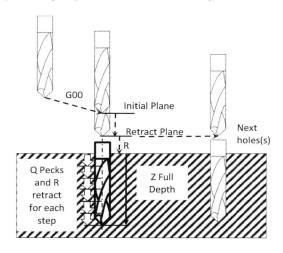

Figure 4.22 G73 Commands Example and tool motion

G73 Command Example:

N80 G98 G73 X-0.5 Y-0.5 Z-0.9 Q0.0312 R0.2 F3.4

Return to retract plane R0.2, Deep Hole Drill canned cycle, X-0.5 Y-0.5 Z-0.9 R0.2 Peck - Q0.0312 F3.4

G80 Cancel Canned Cycle

Format structure: G80

G80 Cancel canned cycle is used to cancel cycles, like G73, G81, G82, G83, and others, see Figure 4.23. Since a canned cycle will run until stopped, it needs to be canceled to avoid problems. It is also routine G80 to be placed at the beginning of the program to remove any remaining canned cycles. Note that Return to Home Position G28 command does not cancel the canned cycle; therefore, G80 must be used before invoking G28 or any tool changes.

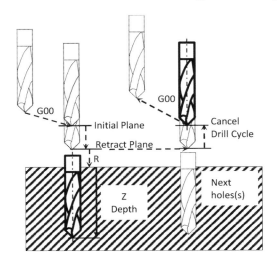

Figure 4.23 G80 Commands Example and tool motion

G80 command example:

N120 G80   **Cancel Drill canned cycle**

G81 Drilling Cycle

Format structure: G81 X_ Y_ Z_ R_ K_ F_

G81 drilling cycle is used to drill multiple holes at specific locations listed within the cycle by coordinates after it, see Figure 4.24. In the drilling cycle of G81, X defines coordinate of the first hole in the X-axis, Y defines the coordinate of the first hole in the Y-axis, Z defines the depth of the hole (the tool will travel to Z depth with the federate F), R defines the position of the retract plane, and F defines the feed rate for hole machining. The G81 cycle defines the location of the first hole; the machines will continue to drill holes according to the coordinates specified bellow G81 until the cycle is canceled with the G80 cycle cancel command. All of the holes in the cycle are machining with the feed rate F, specified in the G81 cycle block.

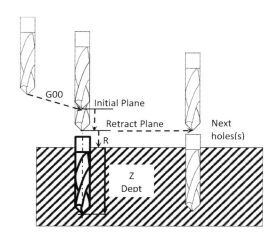

Figure 4.24 G81 Commands Example and tool motion

G81 Command Example:

N80 G98 G81 X-1.5 Y1. Z-0.5 R0.2 F3.4   **Return to retract plane R0.2, Drill canned cycle, X-1.5 Y1. Z-0.5 R0.2 F3.4**

G82 Spot/Counter Boring Cycle

Format structure: G82 X_ Y_ Z_ R_ P_K_ F_

G82 spot drilling or counter boring cycle, similar to G81, is used to drill multiple holes at specific locations listed within the cycle by coordinates after it with dwell at the bottom of the hole, see Figure 4.25. In the spot/counter boring drilling cycle of G82, X defines coordinate of the first hole in X-axis, Y defines the coordinate of the first hole in Y-axis, Z defines the depth of the hole (the tool will travel to Z depth with the federate F), R defines the position of the retract plane, P defines the dwell time in milliseconds, and F defines the feed rate for hole machining. The dwell pauses the feed rate movement at the bottom of the hole while the spindle still rotates; this allows the tool to clear the bottom surface of the hole. G82 cycle defines the location of the first hole; the machines will continue to drill holes according to the coordinates specified bellow G82 until the cycle is canceled with the G80 cycle cancel command. All of the holes in the cycle are machining with the feed rate F, specified in the G82 cycle block.

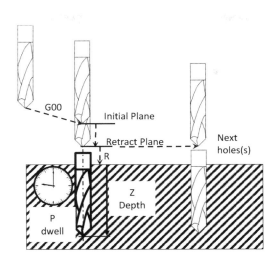

Figure 4.25 G82 Commands Example and tool motion

G82 Command Example:

N80 G98 G82 X-0.5 Y-0.5 Z-0.6 R0.2   Return to retract plane R0.2, Spot drill canned
P1000 F3.   cycle, X-1.5 Y1. Z-0.5 R0.2 F3.

G83 Deep Hole Drilling Cycle

Format structure: G83 X_ Y_ Z_ R_ Q_ K_ F_

G83 Deep hole drilling cycle includes peck drilling on each hole; it is used for deep drill multiple holes at specific locations listed within the cycle by coordinates after the cycle, see Figure 4.26. In the Deep drilling cycle G83, X defines coordinate of the first hole in the X-axis, Y defines the coordinate of the first hole in the Y-axis, Z defines the full depth of the hole (tool will travel to Z depth with the federate F), R defines the position of the retract plane, Q pecking defines the incremental drilling distance on individual pecks (depth with the federate F), and F defines the feed rate for hole machining. After each peck drilling movement, the tool moves back rapidly to the retract plane R and repeats this pecking cycle until it reaches the full depth Z of the hole. The pecking drilling cycle allows the removal of chips from the hole after each peck; this permits machining of deep holes without breaking the tool. G83 cycle defines the location of the first hole; the machines will continue to drill holes according to the coordinates specified bellow G83 until the cycle is canceled with the G80 cycle cancel command. All of the holes in the cycle are machining with the feed rate F, and pecking settings specified in the G83 cycle block.

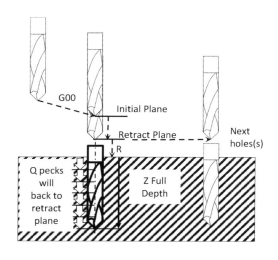

Figure 4.26 G83 Commands Example and tool motion

G83 Command Example:

N80 G98 G83 X-1.75 Y-1. Z-1.2
R0.2 Q0.0312 F3.4

Return to retract plane R0.2, Deep Hole Drill canned
cycle, X-1.75 Y1. Z-1.2 R0.2 Peck - Q0.0312 F3.4

G84 Tapping Cycle

Format structure: G84 X_ Y_ Z_ R_ F_

G84 Tapping cycle (also called Rigid tapping cycle) includes making tread with tapping tool rigidly attached to the spindle drilling. Tapping is performed by clockwise rotating the spindle and moving inside the hole direction with synchronous federate; at the bottom of the hole, the spindle stops, reverses its rotation direction to counter clockwise, and move back to the retract plane with the same feed rate. Feed rate is calculated by multiplying rotation RPM speeded by thread pitch. The tapping cycle is used for tapping multiple holes at specific locations listed within the cycle by coordinates after the cycle, see Figure 4.27. In the Tapping cycle G83, X defines coordinate of the first hole in the X-axis, Y defines the coordinate of the first hole in the Y-axis, Z defines the full depth of the hole (the tool will travel to Z depth with the federate F), R defines the position of the retract plane, and F defines the feed rate for hole machining. G84 cycle defines the location of the first hole; the machines will continue to tap holes according to the coordinates specified bellow G84 until the cycle is canceled with theG80 cycle cancel command. All of the holes in the cycle are machining with the same feed rate F, and settings specified in the G84 cycle block.

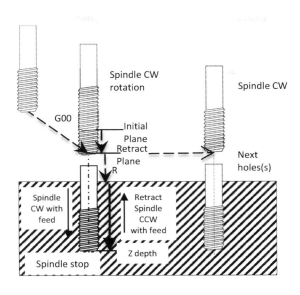

Figure 4.27 G84 Commands Example and tool motion

G84 Command Example:

N80 G98 G84 X-0.5 Y-0.5 Z-0.5 R0.2 F25. **Tapping canned cycle, X-0.5 Y-0.5 Z-0.5 R0.2 F25.**

G90 Absolute Programming

Format structure: G90

G90 defines the coordinate position from the origin of the part coordinate system, specified during the CNC mill set up, typically set up on the front, top side of the workpiece. All motions of the machine positive (+) or negative (-) are references from the part origin. Absolute programming is the most commonly used in industry, allowing programming without errors since the coordinates are explicitly specified for each motion. G90is a modal command and remains active until incremental coordinate G91 is specified. G90 and G91 can be used in the same program.

G90 Command Example:

N10 G90 G20 G49 G40 G80   **Absolute programming,** Inch Units, Cancel offsets

G91 Incremental Programming

Format structure: G91

G91 defines the incremental position movement from the previous position of the part. The first point of the incremental position is a reference from the origin of the coordinate system. All motions of the machine positive (+) or negative (-) are reference from the previous position.

Incremental programming is not often used in the industry. The command is a modal and remains active until absolute coordinate G90 is specified. G91 and G90 can be used in the same program multiple times.

G91 Command Example:

N82 G91   Incremental programming

G98 Initial Plane Return

Format structure: G98 _

G98 initial plane return in the drilling cycle is used to return the tool to the Z position of the initial plane after drilling all the holes specified in the drill cycle, see Figure 4.28. The Z position of the tool before starting the initial plane's drilling cycle is the one that tool returns after the cycle if G98 is specified. Since the retract plane's position is defined in the cycle, G98 leads to an additional rapid movement to the Z coordinate of this initial plane.

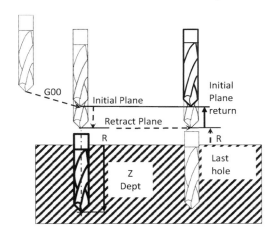

Figure 4.28 G98 Commands Example and tool motion

G98 Command Example:

N60 G00 Z0.6   **Rapid move to Initial plane Z0.6**
N70 G98 G81 X-0.5 Y-1. Z-0.65 R0.2 F3.4   **Return to initial plane Z0.6 after return to**
                                                   retract plane R0.2, X-0.5 Y-1. Z-0.65 R0.2 F3.4

G99 Retract Plane Return

Format structure: G99 _

G99 retract plane return in the drilling cycle is used to return the tool to the Z position of the retract plane after drilling all the holes specified in the drill cycle, see Figure 4.29. The Z position of the tool before starting the drilling cycle retract plane is the one that tool returns after the cycle G99 is specified. Since the position of the retract plane R-value is defined in the cycle, G99 leads to rapid movement to Z coordinate of this retract plane.

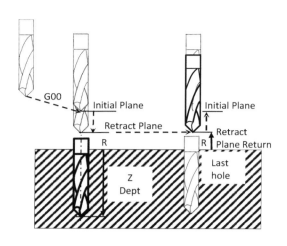

Figure 4.29 G99 Commands Example and tool motion

G99 Command Example:

N80 G99 G81 X-0.4 Y-0.4 Z-0.65 R0.2 F3.   **Return to retract plane R0.2, Drill canned cycle**
                                                X-0.4 Y-0.4 Z-0.65 R0.2 F3.

M00 Program Stop

Format structure: M00

M00 Program stop is used when a temporary stop needs to be performed during the CNC machining process. When the M00 command block is reached, the CNC controller stops temporary all essential functions like the spindle rotation, coolant, all axis motions, and others. M00 does not terminate the program execution but is used to temporarily stop the program execution so the operator can check or adjust the machine, like coolant hose direction, tool wear or breakage, machined surface size, and finish and to remove chips from working zone and others. The program is resumed normally when the operator presses the cycle start. All settings and orders of the operations, including coordinate positions, feed rate, speed, and other., remain unchanged after resuming the program execution.

M00 Command Example:

N130 M00   **Program Stop**

M01 Optional Program Stop

Format structure: M01

M01 Optional Program stop is used when a temporary stop needs to be performed during the CNC machining process. When the M01 command block is reached, the CNC controller stops temporary all essential functions like the spindle rotation, coolant, all axis motions, and others. M01 does not terminate the program execution but is used to temporarily stop the program execution so the operator can check or adjust the machine, like coolant hose direction, tool wear or breakage, machined surface size, and finish and to remove chips from working zone and others. The program is resumed normally when the operator presses the cycle start. All settings and orders of the operations, including coordinate positions, feed rate, speed, and others., remain unchanged after resuming the program execution.

M01 works the same way as the M00 program stop when an optional M01 switch on the control panel is activated. When the optional button M01 is not active, the M01 optional stop is ignored by the controller, and the program executes normally without any stop function. The M01 optional stop is useful when an initial program is created and refined, allowing troubleshooting program errors, and restoring the normal execution cycle later when the problem is resolved.

M01 Command Example:

N130 M01   **Optional program stop**

M02 Program End

Format structure: M02

M02 defines the end of the program execution, terminated the program. M02 is the last block of the CNC programs. After the M02, the CNC controlled switches off all operations – spindle rotation all axis feed fate and rapid movements, and others.

M02 Command Example:

N160 M02　　　　　**Program end**

M03 Spindle Clockwise Rotation (CW)

Format structure: M03 S__ (S__M3)

M03 defines the clockwise spindle rotation (CW); it is usually issued together with spindle speed rotation S_ defines by a number following it (e.g., S3000). M03 is active until the spindle is stopped by the M05 command or program ended. The CNC controller will stop the spindle before the tool is changed and will restart the spindle rotation after tool changes. If the spindle stops in a program, M03 will reactivate the rotation with the same rotation speed defined before stopping the spindle.

M03 Command Example:

N30 S3060 M03　　　　**RPM speed 3060, Spindle Clockwise Rotation (CW)**

M04 Spindle Counter Clockwise Rotation (CCW)

Format structure: M04 S__(S__ M4)

M04 (similar to M03) defines the spindle counter clockwise rotation (CCW); it is usually issued together with spindle speed rotation S__ defines by a number following it (e.g., S4000). M04 is active until the spindle is stopped by the M05 command or program ended. The CNC controller will stop the spindle before the tool is changed and will restart the spindle rotation after tool changes. If the spindle stops in a program, M04 will reactivate the rotation with the same rotation speed defined before stopping the spindle.

M04 Command Example:

N30 S3060 M04　　　　**RPM speed 3060, Spindle Counter Clockwise Rotation (CCW)**

M05 Spindle Stop

Format structure: M05

M05 stops the spindle rotation. It is used to stop the spindle rotation of the end of the program permanently. Other M command like M00, M01, and M02 stop the spindle temporarily, allowing to restart the rotation.

M05 Command Example:

N160 M05   **Stop spindle**

M06 Tool change

Format structure: M06_ T_

M06 tool change is issued together with the tool number. During the machine tools, set up the tool parameters, radius, and length offset value are saved in the tool setup table, inside the CNC computer control. The tool change includes several commands. At first, the spindle is stopped and moved to the position for the tool changes; second, the tool in the spindle is removed and placed in its position in the automatic tool changer (ATC); third, a new tool is placed inside the spindle and locked. When a CNC machine doesn't have ATC, the controller stops the spindle and sends a message to the screen for tool change; then, the operator manually replaces the tool, and the work continues after cycle start (Enter or continue, depending on the CNC system) command is reactivated.

M06 command example:

N20 T1 G43 H02 M06   **Tool change Tool#1, length offset #1)**
......
N200 T2 G43 H01 M06   **Tool change Tool#2, length offset #2**

M08 Coolant Start

Format structure: M08

M08 command starts the cutting fluid (coolant) flow. It is advisable to start the cutting fluid just before the first cutting occurred. Cutting fluid is essential in cutting most metal alloys; it cools the workpiece and tool material, provides lubrication, and removes chips away from the working area.

M08 Command Example:

N40 M08   **Coolant start**

M09 Coolant Off

Format structure: M09

M09 command switches off the cutting fluid (coolant) flow. It is advisable to stop the cutting fluid just after the last cutting occurred. Depending on the CNC controller, the coolant is automatically switched off before/after the tool change, at program stop or end. Refer to the operating manual for details regarding the starting or stopping the cutting fluid flow within the program.

M09 Command Example:

N120 M9   Coolant off

M30 Program End and Rewind to the Beginning

Format structure: M30

M30 defines the end of the program execution, terminated the program, and rewind to the beginning (return the program cursor to the begging of the program). It can be used when multiple identical parts are produced one after another. M30 is the last block of the CNC programs. After M30, the CNC controlled switches off all operations. It stops spindle rotation, all axis feed fate, and rapid movements, and others.

M30 Command Example:

N210 M30   **End of the program and rewind to the beginning**

M98 Call Subprogram

Format structure: M98P__

The M98 calls subprogram (also called subroutine). When M98 with number P____ is called from a program, it transfers the control of all operations to the subprogram the number defined by P__. After the completion of the subprogram, it returns the control to the main program with command M99. The subprogram can be placed in the same main program (then it is active only within this program) or separate external CNC program. Also, subprograms can be called many times from the same program. When a separate subprogram is used, it can be called from any program.

M98 Command Example:

N90 M98 P2020   **Call subprogram number 2020**

M99 Return from Subprogram

Format structure: M99

The M99 return from the subprogram (also called subroutine). M99 is called at the end of the subprogram and return control to the main program. The subprogram can be placed inside (usually after the end) in the same main program (then it can be called only within this program) or separate external CNC program. Subprograms can be called many times from the same program. When a separate subprogram is used, it can also be called from any program.

M99 Command Example:

N29040 M99   **Return from subprogram**

/ Block skip

Format structure: */ N (before the program number)*

Skip the running of the same block after it is used. It must be specified on the most left position before the block number.

/ (Block Skip) Command Example:

/N330 G00 X-0.5 Y-0.5   **Block Skip Rapid move to X-0.5 Y-0.5**

Block skip, also called block delete, is used to skip the running of the block after it is used. It is active when the block skip button on the CNC control panel is pressed. This option is used to program a group of similar parts with small differences in futures. For example, block skip can be used for the section of the program than needs to be omitted when a certain future is no needed to be machined and can be activated when desired. If the block skip button is not activated, the program is executed in the regular sequence.

(__ __ __ __) Comments

(__ __ __ __) Format structure: (Comment text)

Comments are placed between parenthesis "()" when there is a need to explain the program block or add additional information on running or set up. It can be specified on any block when needed. It is a useful practice, similar to the one used by computer code programmers, which can make the program readable easily to understand and run. Properly used, the comment is completely ignored by the CNC controller, even if it contains G and M code inside the text, and it is treated the same as empty spaces inside the program.

(_ _ _) Comment Command Example:

N10 G90 G00 G17 G49 G40 G80   (Inch Units, Absolute programming)

Notes:

Notes:

Chapter 5

CNC Programming with Autodesk Inventor:

Introduction to CAD Design

Autodesk Inventor CAD and Inventor CAM (HMS) Solid Modeling

There are many tutorials and books for Inventor solid modeling and drafting. Here will limit the explanation about creating simple solid models and profiles to be machined with CNC machine tools.

Create a new file

Start Inventor and *Create a new file*, select *Standard.ipt*

Sketch

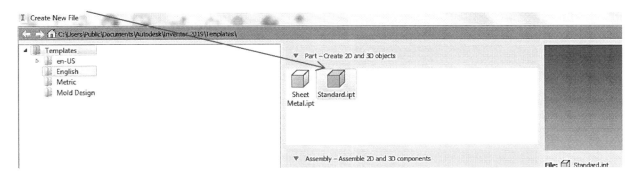

We will start the part creation with a sketch on the XY plane. Under the *Part1*, menu click on →*Origin*, then on *XY Plane* to select the drawing plane.

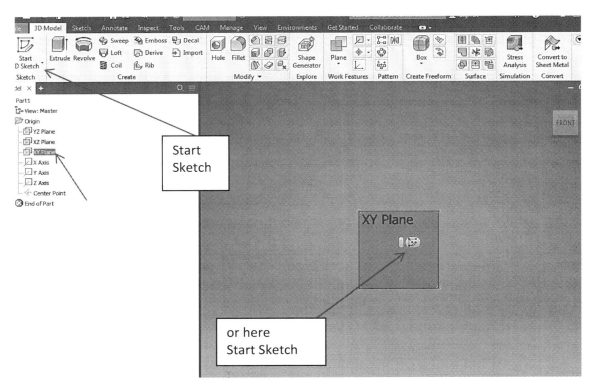

Click on *Start* Sketch on the top menu *or* the *XY Plane* inside the model window to create a sketch on XY Plane.

Create a rectangle by selecting the rectangle feature (1) and then select the *Start point* and on the diagonal *End point* of the rectangle, see the figure bellow. You can resize the rectangle by moving the mouse pointer or type the length (2) and height (3) on the block (use Tab key to switch from one to another). If you didn't manage to define the exact setup dimensions you can always use *Dimension* constraint and modify each dimension by typing the desired number.

To complete the sketch, click on *Finish Sketch Exit* with green checkmark, on the top right corner.

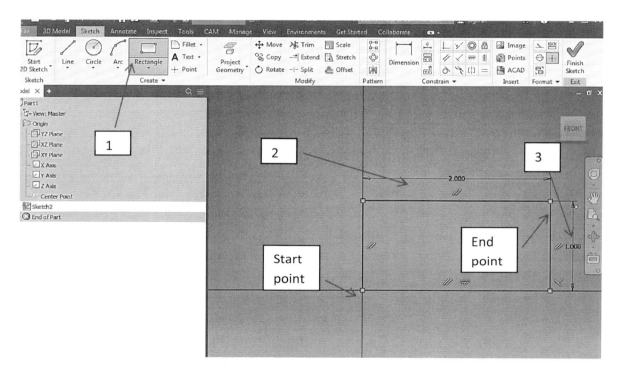

Extrusion

Then select the *3D Model* menu, click on *Extrude icon,* type the distance (3/4 in), and click on *OK*. The solid model of the rectangular block is completed.

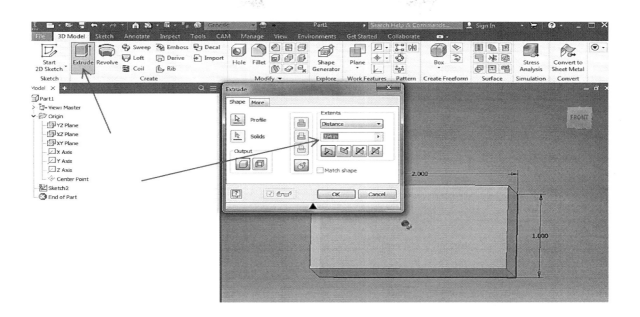

Similarly, you can create circular or other enclosed profiles by using a combination of lines. To extrude any shape to a solid model, the profile must be completely enclosed.

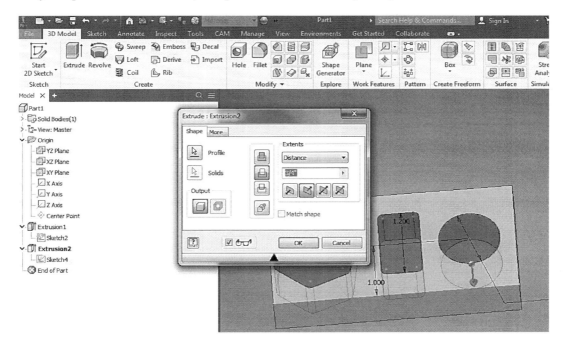

Extrusion direction can be reversed or it can be applied in both directions. Instead of the extrusion, the profile can be used for *Cutting* or *Intersection* with other solid. If there are two enclosed profiles, the extrusion can be selected be between them (then the internal profile extrusion became void); refer to the Inventor *Help/Tutorial* menu for more information. After completing the modeling, save the file on the folder of your choice.

Notes:

Chapter 6

CNC Programming with Inventor CAM:

Introduction to CNC Machining

Introduction to Inventor CAM machining

CAM functions are shown on the CAM menu with graphical representations of different operations. We will explain the necessary steps for primary milling operations in more detail. We will begin by defining the stock and the origin of the part to be machined.

Setup

Select the *Setup* menu, then select the *Stock* tab and leave the default value of *Mode: Relative size box*. The stock is added with default values from *Size offset* and *Top offset*; you can change them to the desired size. Next, select the *Setup* tab to change the position of the coordinate system.

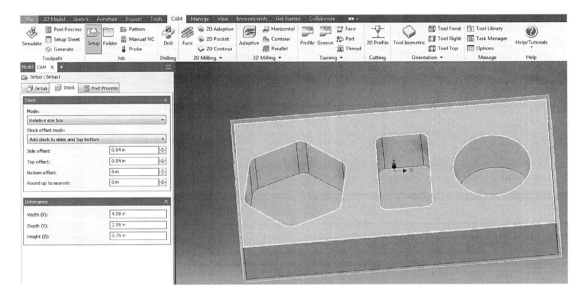

For the CAM part, we can use the original design coordinate system as default for the part coordinate system. In most cases, we will need to select a part coordinate system suitable for machining, here are the necessary steps:

Under the *Origin:* choose from the pulldown menu, *Selected point,* and click on a point on the part (e.g., top left corner). The origin will move to that point, if the orientations of X, Y Z axis are not on the desired direction, use the pulldown menu under the *Orientation:* to revert to the desired direction. Note that Z-axis must be pointed toward the direction of the tool that will be used. For this setup example, all the coordinates in machining will be referenced from this origin. If you need to rotate or move the part to a new position(s), you can create a new setup(s) for that position(s). Finish the Setup, click OK, a new *CAM* tab is created next to the *Model* tab.

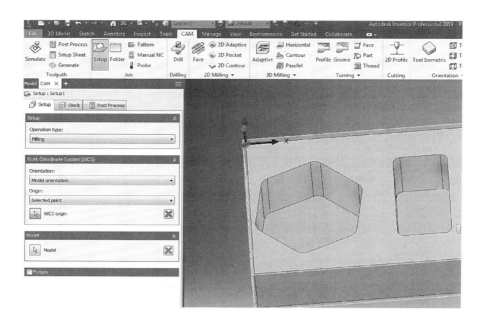

The next step is creating the tool paths that can be *Drilling*, *2D Milling*, *3D Milling,* or *Turning*. Each CAM process has several options that can be selected depending on the desired operation. We will start with a *Face* operation, a part of *2D Milling*.

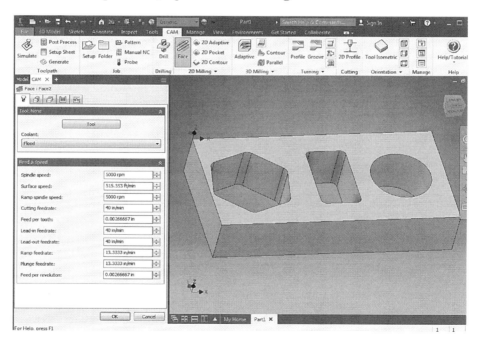

2D Milling

There are several most common *2D Milling* operations in Inventor CAM, shown on the ribbon menu: *Face, 2D Adaptive, 2D Pocket, 2D Contour*. Additional operations are available by selecting the *2D Milling* pulldown menu: *Slot, Track, Thread, Circular, Bore,* and *Engrave*.

2D Face

Select *Face* from *CAM* menu, a new Face: sub-window appears with several tabs, the first is the *Tool*. We need to select a tool from the library. On the left side, there are *All Tools* and *Sample library* with submenus. Select *Sample Library* →*Tutorial-inch (or other)*, then on the right window select tool **#1-Ø2" face (2" Face Mill)** and finish by clicking *Select* on the bottom right. The new tool is selected, and its number and size appear next to *Tool: #1-Ø2" face (2" Face Mill)*.

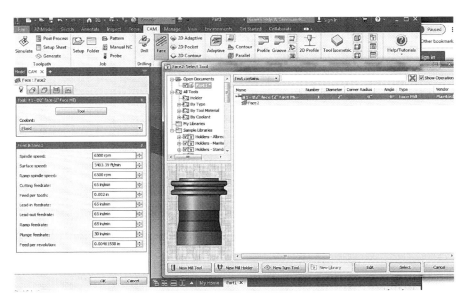

Next to the *Tool* tab are *Stock, Contours, Clearance Height, Passes*, and *Linking* menus, which will not be altered for this operation. We will explain more detail for each tab when we use them with other operations later.

Compete this operation by clicking on *OK* on the bottom of the right sub-window. Now the new operation *[T1] Face2* is created under the *Setup1*. It has submenus Tool number, WCS, and size of the program in bytes. If you select the *[T1] Face2,* the tool path profile (blue/green lines) will show on the main window.

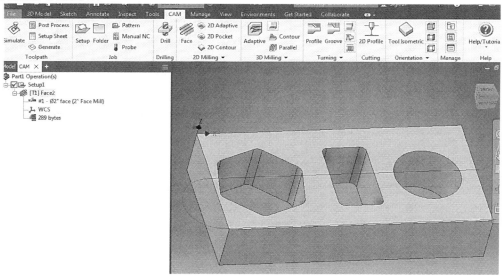

Simulation

Further, we can simulate the facing operation by selecting *Simulate* on the main tab. New simulation windows pop up, with the tool and the tool path on the top of the part. You can run the simulation by pressing the big arrow on the video/VCR like play menu. The green timeline below shows the progress. You can automatically run the simulation, adjust the speed using the white slider under the control arrows, or run manually by advancing the green timeline. The simulation display can be modified to show the *Tool Shaft, Tool Holder, Show transparent*. If you want to see, the machining starting from the stock, select the *Stock* submenu on lect lower

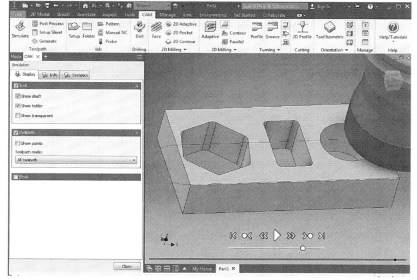

side. To return to the *CAM* menu, click on the *Close* button at the bottom of the left sub-window. Save the Inventor file that now includes your CAM toolpath and simulation.

Post Processing

Now we are ready to create a CNC program that can be used for machining on an actual CNC machine. The postprocessor translates CL (cutter location) and movements to a CNC program, also called G code, for the selected machine. The program contains a group of codes and parameters necessary to run the machine, placed in the required format and order, and ready to be used by the CNC machine controller. Even the CNC code is standardized, each CNC

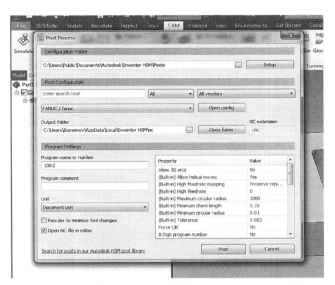

machine controller requires its own postprocessor. We will use one of the most common Fanuc Co., postprocessor.

To create CNC code, select the operation, click on *Post Processor* on the top of the menu tab. A new pop up window appears. Click on the machine selection pull downmenu (next to Open Config button) and Select FANUC/Fanuc. You can change the *Output folder*, the *Program name or number* from the default 1001. Click on the *Post* button and to save the program.

A new window, *Autodesk HSN Edit (CAM)* Edit pops up with your program inside. Different color indicates different codes in the program to make it easy to understand its structure. You can Stroll down/up, modify the program, and save it like using a regular text editor. Some versions of the Inventor Editor have a *Backplot* function, which can show the tool path.

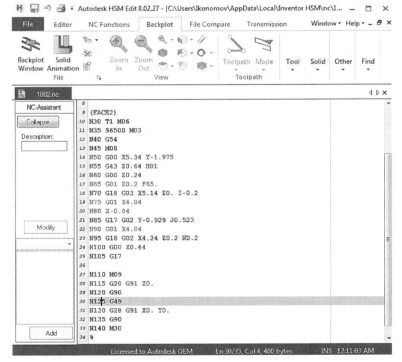

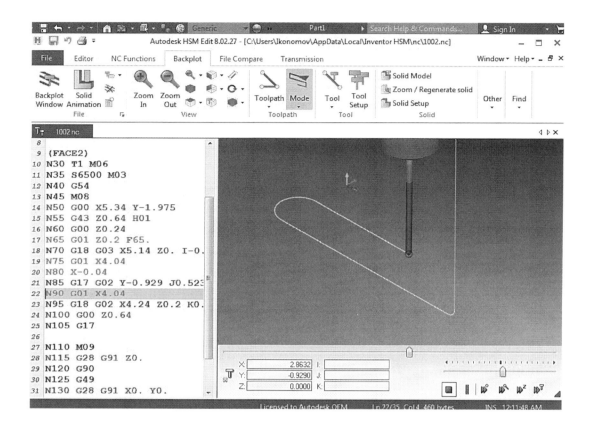

After clicking on the *Backplot Window,* a new toolpath simulation window appears on the right side, next to the CNC program.

Simulation of the tool movement can be run from the controller, operated as a video/VCR controller.

The *Editor* also has a *Transmission* function to send/receive programs to/from the CNC controller, if the computer is connected to it via network or serial communication cable. To use this function, the *DNC Setup* needs to be set to the proper transmission protocol. Refer to your CNC controller operation manual for setting details.

2D Contour

We will use a similar setup as in the *Face* operation above. Select *2D Contour* from the *CAM* menu, a new *2D Contour*: *2D Contour 1* sub-window appears with several tabs, the first is the Tool. The tool selected is the one from the facing operation.

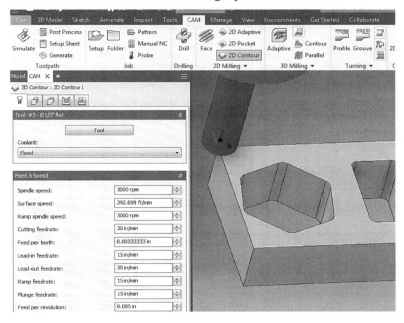

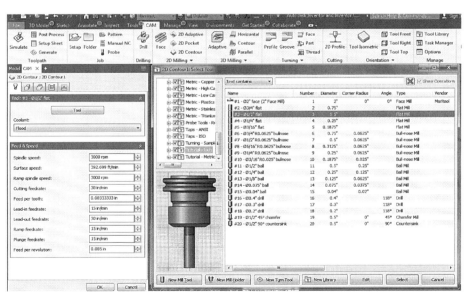

We need to select a new tool from the library for contour operation. On the left side, there are *All Tools* and *Sample library* with submenus. Select *Sample Library →Tutorial-inch*, the on the right window select tool **#3-Ø1/2" flat (1/2" Flat Mill)** and finish by clicking *Select* on the bottom right.

Now the tool is selected, and the number and size appear next to it *Tool: #3-Ø 1/2" flat*.

Next to *Tool* tab select Geometry and click on edge at the bottom contour of the part, it will change the color to blue when selected.

The rest of the tabs Height, Passes, and Linking menus will not be modified for this part of the operation. More detail for each tab will be given later with other operations.

To complete the operation, click OK on the bottom of the left sub-window. Now the operation [*T3]2D Contour* is created under the Face operation as part of the *Setup1*. It has submenus Tool number, WCS, and size of the program in bytes. If you select [*T3]2D Contour,* the tool path profile will show in the main window. Note that this process show machining at full hight of the part without stepdown and roughing operations.

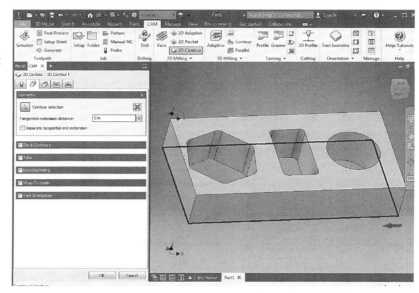

Since the cutting high is too big, can modify the contour program for multiple depths. Double click (or right-click and Edit) on the new [*T3]2D Contour,* select the fourth tab, *Passes,* and scroll down to be able to see the *Multiple Dept* and check it to activate the extended menu. The first value *Maximum roughing stepdown (0.04")* defines how much down the tool to go on each step, note that the *Finishing stepdown* 0.008 is less to produce clear finishing cut at the bottom. Leave the rest of the values as suggested by the software and click on *OK* to finish the modification.

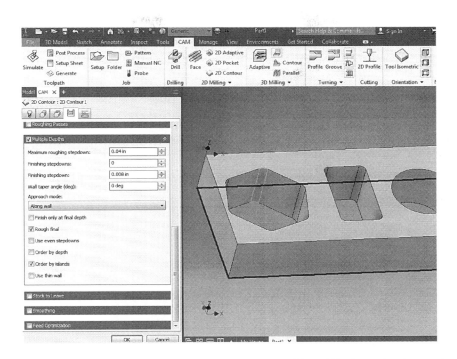

If you select [*T3]2D Contour* again, the new tool path profile will show in the main window. Note that this process show machining multiple steps for the roughing operations and finishing operation.

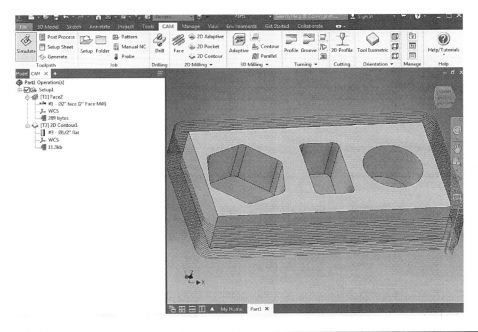

Simulation

Now we can simulate the 2D contour milling process by selecting *Simulate* on the main tab. A new simulation window pops up with the tool and the tool path on the top of the part. You can run the simulation by pressing big arrows control buttons to play. The green timeline shows the progress, and you can run automatically, adjust the speed using the slide under the control arrow, or run manually by advancing the green timeline. To go back to the *CAM* menu, click on *the Close* button at the bottom of the left sub-window. If you want to see all machining processes in one simulation, select the *Setup1* and rerun the Simulate. Save the Inventor file that now includes two CAM simulations.

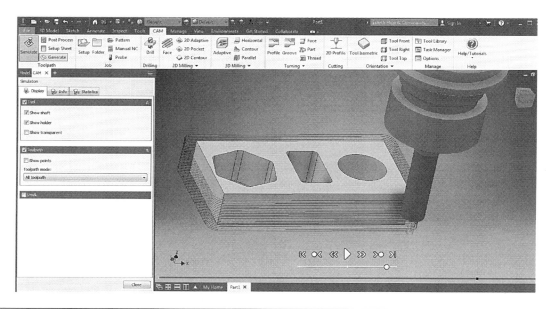

Post Processing

Now we are ready to create the next CNC program. Select the *2D Contour operation* click on the *Post Processor* on the top of the menu tab. Click on the pulldown menu and select FANUC/Fanuc (next to Open Config button). In the *Program name or number* slot, change the program to the desired number (e.g.1002). Remember the program numbers and the folder where you saved your program. Click on *Post* to save the program to the desired folder.

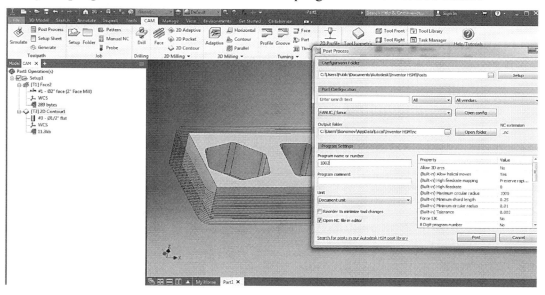

A new window *Autodesk CAM (HSM) Edit* pops up with your new program inside. If the Backlot is selected, the postprocessor simulation windows show on the right. If you want to see all machining processes in one program, select the *Setup1* and run the on *Post Processor*, then save to new program number. The program will contain contour operations, including tool information.

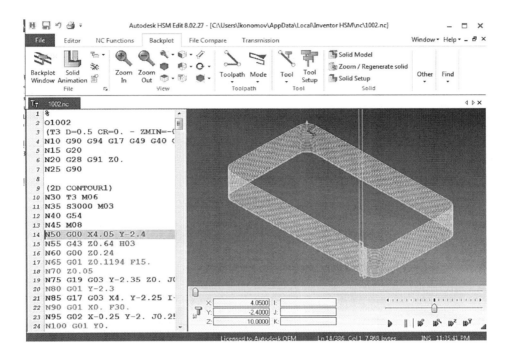

2D Pocket

We will use the same setup as the *Face* and *Contour* operations above. Select *2D Pocket* from the *CAM* menu, a new *2D Pocket*: *2D Pocket 2* sub-window appears with several tabs, the first one is the Tool. The default tool selected is the one from the previous operation. To choose a new tool, select tool **#4-Ø1/4" flat (1/4" Flat Mill)** and finish by clicking *Select* on the bottom right.

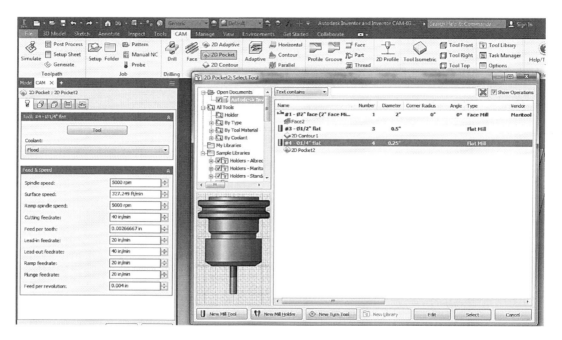

The tool selected with its number and size appears next to *Tool: #4-Ø 1/4" flat.* Select *Geometry* next to the *Tool* tab, click on the *Pocket selection,* and select the bottom hexagon hole of the part; it will change the color to blue when selected. You can select multiple 2D pockets, let select square and cylindrical pockets as well.

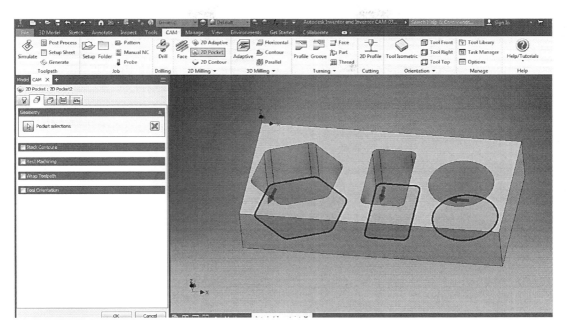

The rest of the tabs *Height*, *Passes*, and *Linking* menus will not be modified for this part of the operation. More detail for each tab will be given later with other operations.

Let complete the operation by clicking *OK* on the bottom left side of the 2D pocket sub-window. Now the operation [*T4]2D Pocket 2* is created under the *2D Contour* operation as part of the *Setup1*. It has submenus Tool number, WCS, and size of the program in bytes. If you select [*T4]2D Pocket,* the tool path profile will show in the main window. Note that this process shows machining at the full height of the part with a red spiral path showing tool movement to reach the bottom of the part. Here we assume that pocket is machined from a solid material; therefore, a trough steps downhole needs to be created not to break the tool. You can modify the program to use multiple depths and explain the spiral path setup.

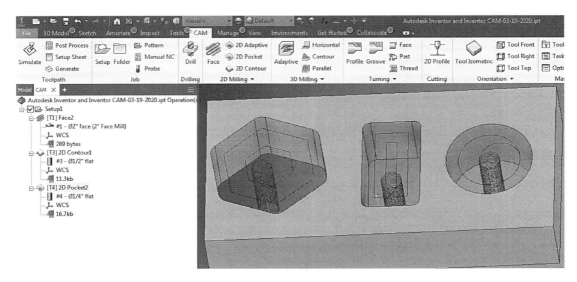

Double click (or right-click and Edit) on the new [*T4*]*2D Pocket2,* select the fourth tab, *Passes,* and scroll down to be able to see the *Multiple Dept* and check it to activate the extended menu. Keep the *Maximum roughing stepdown (0.04")* and the *Finishing stepdown* 0.008. Leave the rest of the parameters unchanged and click on *OK* to finish the modification. If you select [*T4*]*2D Pocket2* again, the tool path profile will show in the main window. Note that this process show machining of pockets with multiple steps.

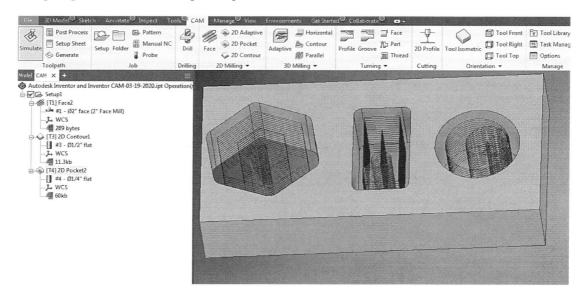

Simulation

We can simulate all the 2D pockets processes by selecting *Simulate* on the main tab. A new simulation window pops up, and the control buttons are the same as described above. Click on the *Close* button and go back to the *CAM* menu. Save the Inventor file that now includes three CAM simulations.

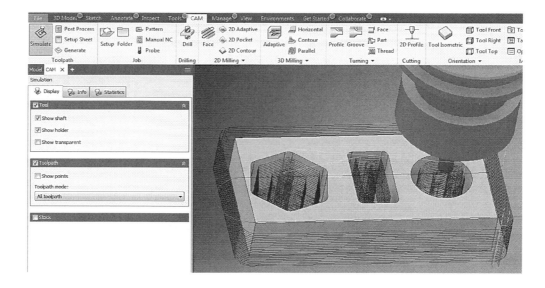

Now we are ready to create the CNC program. Select the operation click on the *Post Processor* on the top of the menu tab. Click on the pulldown menu and Select FANUC/Fanuc (next to Open Confi button). In the *Program name or number* slot, change the program to 1004 or other number. Remember the number and where you saved your program. Click on *Post* to save the program to the desired Folder. This time we will create all machining processes in one program. Select the *Setup1* and run the on *Post Processor*, save to new program number 1004. The program will contain two operations, facing and contour, including all tool changes.

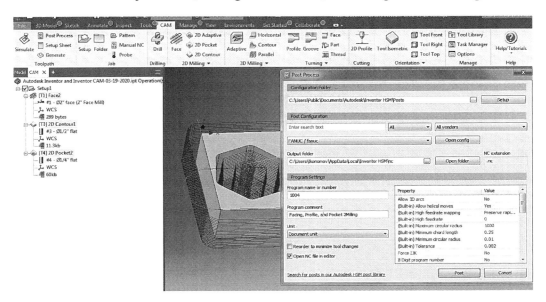

A new window *Autodesk Edit CAM (HSM) Edit* pops up with your new program inside. If the *Backlot* is selected, the postprocessor simulation window shows on the right.

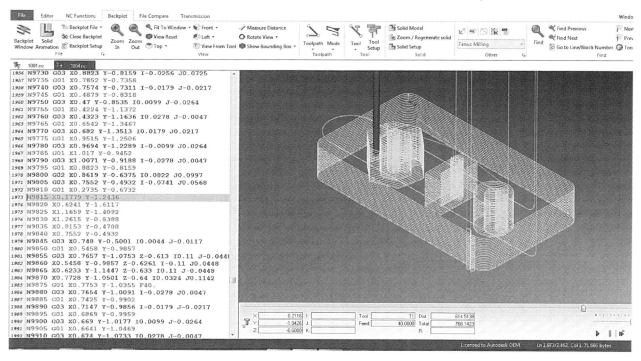

This section concludes the introduction to Inventor HSM (CAM) 2D Milling. For more information, refer to the Help menu or tutorials on the AUTODESK web site.

Notes:

Notes:

Chapter 7

CNC Programming with Inventor CAM:

Advanced 2D Machining

Inventor CAM additional 2D milling

To explain all 2D milling operations in detail, we will use a new, more complex model with several futures. We will explain ho to do 2D machining for 2D Adaptive, Slot, Trace, Thread, Circular, Bore, Engrave, and Chamfer function of Inventor CAM.

Due to the complexity of the model, we will open an existing model *Connecting rod,* and gradually we will work on machining 2D and 3D features. If you need more information how to design CAD models in Inventor refer to Autodesk webs side.

Setup

Again we will begin by defining the stock and the origin of the part to be machined. Select the CAM tab. Click on *Setup*, then *Stock,* and leave the default value of *Model: Relative size box.* The stock is added with default values from *Size offset* and *Top offset*; you can change them to the desired size. Next, select the *Setup* tab to change the position of the coordinate system.

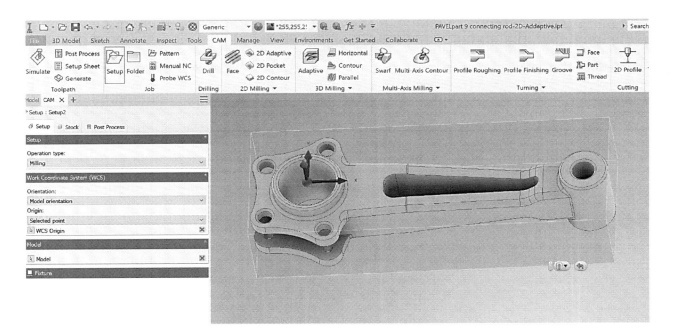

The CAM part will use the original designed coordinate system as default for the part coordinate system. In most cases, we will need to select a part coordinate system suitable for machining; here are the steps:

On the menu *Origin:* from the pulldown menu choose *Select point,* and click on a point on the part (e.g., top left cylinder). The origin will move to that point, if the orientations of X, Y Z axis are not on the desired direction, use *Orientation*: to revert to the desired direction. For this setup example, all the coordinates in machining will be referenced from this origin. If you need to rotate or move the part to a new position(s), you can create a new setup(s) for that position(s). Finish the Setup, click OK, a new *CAM* tab is created next to the *Model* tab.

The next step is creating the tool paths that can be *2D Milling*, *3D Milling,* or *Turning*. Each CAM process has several options that can be selected depending on the desired operation. We will start with a *2D Adaptive* operation, a part of *2D Milling*.

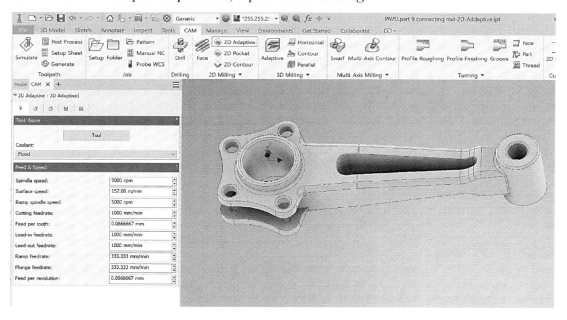

2D Adaptive

Select *2D Adaptive* from the *CAM* menu, a new *2D Adaptive: 2D Adaptive* sub-window appears with several tabs, and the first one is the *Tool*. Click on the *Tool* button. This time we will use metric tools.

We need to select a tool from the library. On the left side, there are *All Tools* and *Sample library*

with submenus. Select *Sample Library→Tutorial-inch (or other)*, then on the right window select tool **#3-Ø10mm flat (10mm flat mill)** and finish by clicking *Select* on the bottom right. The new tool is selected, and its number and size appear next to *Tool: #3-Ø10mm flat*.

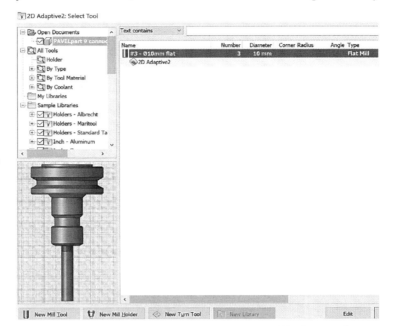

Select *Geometry* next to the *Tool* tab, click on the *Pocket selection,* and select the top left flat surface; it will change the color to blue when selected. You can choose multiple 2D pockets; let select the right cylinder top and flat surface next to it. This machining operation will only machine flat type of surfaces. Later we will discuss how to machine *3D Adaptive* surfaces.

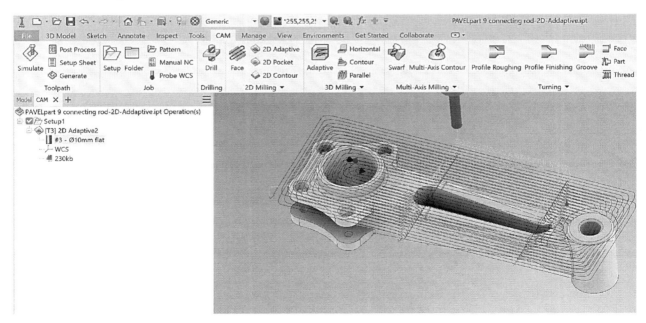

The rest of the tabs *Height*, *Passes*, and *Linking* menus will not be modified for this part of the operation. More detail for each tab will be given later with other operations.

Compete the operation by clicking *OK* on the bottom left side of the 2D Adaptive sub-window. Now the operation *[T3]2D Adaptive2* is created as part of the *Setup1*. It has submenus Tool number, WCS, and size of the program in bytes. If you select *[T3]2D Adaptive2,* the tool paths will show on the main window. Note that this process is machining at the full height on the flat surfaces we selected to the top surfaces of the part. Here we assume that pocket is machined from a solid material. You can modify the program for multiple depths.

Double click (or right-click and Edit) on the new *[T3]2D Adaptive2* menu, select the fourth tab, *Passes,* and scroll down to see the *Multiple Dept* and check it to activate the extended menu. Change the *Maximum roughing stepdown to 3mm* and unselect *Stock to leave*. Leave the rest of the parameters unchanged, then click on *OK* to finish the modification. If you select *[T3]2D Adaptive2* again, the new tool path profile will show in the main window. Note that now the process show machining of pockets with multiple steps.

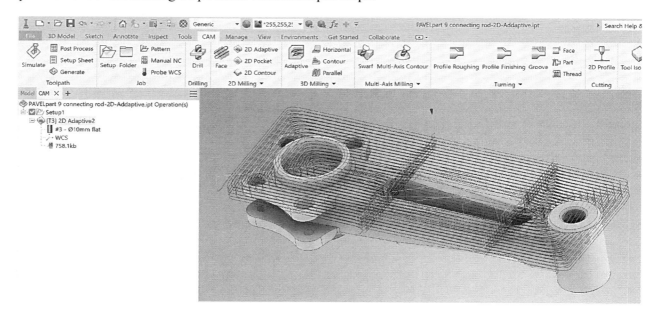

Simulation

We can simulate the *2D Adaptive* by selecting *Simulate* on the main tab. A new simulation window pops up, and the control buttons are the same as described above. You can choose checkbox *Stock* and then select *Material: Show Transparent and Show Part comparison* to see the stock and additional details. Click on the *Close* button and go back to the *CAM* menu. Save the Inventor file that now includes *2D Adaptive* CAM simulation.

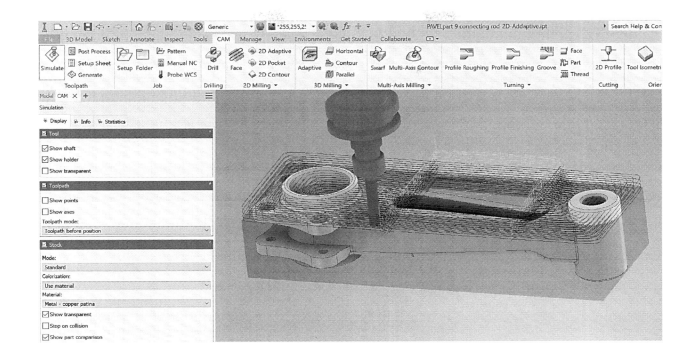

Post Processing

Now we are ready to create the next CNC program. Select the operation click on the *Post Processor* on the top of the menu tab. Click on the pulldown menu and Select FANUC/Fanuc (next to Open Confi button). In the *Program name or number* slot, change the program to 1005 or other number. Remember the numbers and where you saved your program. Click on *Post* to save the program to the desired Folder. This time we will create all machining processes in one program. Select the *Setup1* and run the on *Post Processor*, save to new program number 1005. The program will contain two operations, facing and contour, including all tool changes.

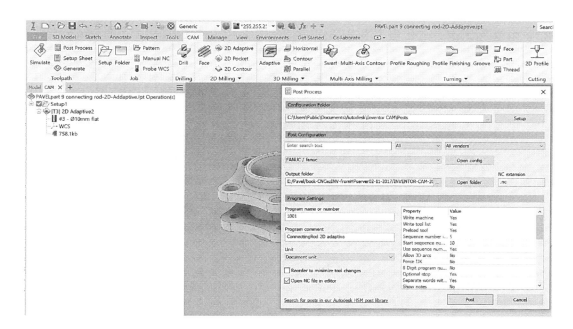

A new window *Autodesk Edit CAM (HSM) Edit* pops up with your new program inside. If the *Backlot* is selected, the postprocessor simulation window shows on the right.

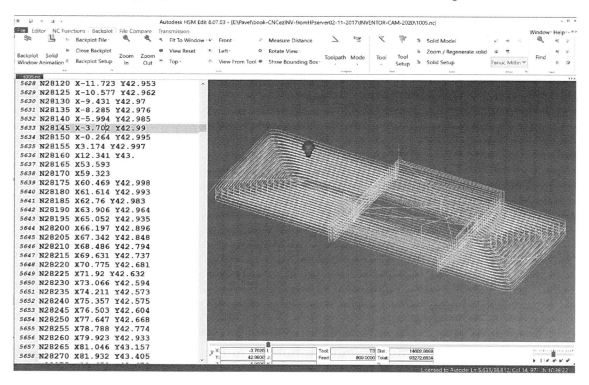

2D Circular

Select *2D Circular* from the *CAM* menu, a new *2D Adaptive: 2D Circular* sub-window appears with several tabs; the first one is the *Tool*, click on the *Tool* button. This time we will use metric tools.

We need to select a tool from the library. On the left side, there are *All Tools* and *Sample libraries* with submenus. On the right side, select the tool **#3-Ø10mm flat (10mm flat mill),** the same one we used in the previous process, and finish it by clicking *Select* on the bottom right. The new tool is selected, and its number and size appear next to *Tool: #3-Ø*10mm flat.

Select *Geometry* next to the *Tool* tab, click on *Circular face selections,* and select the top ring outside of the big cylinder; it will change the color to blue when selected. This machining operation will only machine the outside wall of the cylindrical surface.

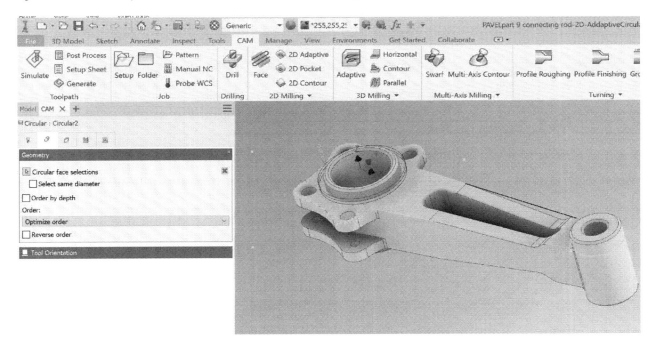

The rest of the tabs *Height*, *Passes*, and *Linking* menus will not be modified for this part of the operation. More detail for each tab will be givenlater with other operations.

Complete the operation by clicking *OK* on the bottom left side of the 2D Circular sub-window. Now the operation *[T3]Circular2* is created as part of the *Setup1*. It has submenus Tool number,

WCS, and size of the program in bytes. If you select *[T3]2D Circular2,* the tool paths will show on the main window. Note that this process is machining at the full hight on the flat surfaces we selected to the top surfaces of the part. Here we assume that pocket is machined from a solid material. We will modify the program for multiple depths.

Double click (or right-click and Edit) on the new *[T3]Circular2* menu, select the fourth tab, *Passes* and scroll down to see the *Multiple Dept* and check it to activate the extended menu. Change the *Maximum roughing stepdown to 3mm* and unselect *Stock to leave.* Leave the rest of the parameters unchanged and click on *OK* to finish the modification. Note that this process show machining of the circular surface with multiple steps.

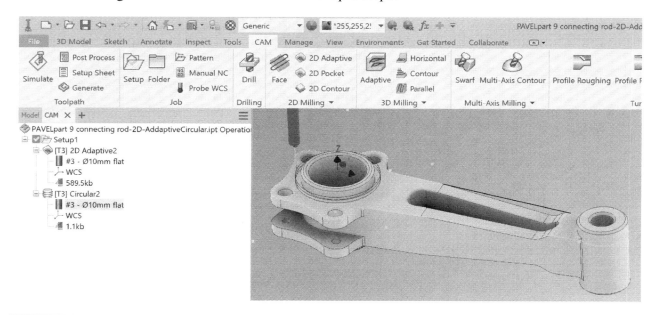

Simulation

We can simulate all the *2D Circular* processes by selecting *Simulate* on the main tab. A new simulation window pops up, and the control buttons are the same as described above. You can select checkbox *Stock* and then select *Material: Show Transparent and Show Part comparison* to see stock and additional details. Click on the *Close* button and go back to the *CAM* menu. Save the Inventor file that now includes *2D Circular* CAM simulation.

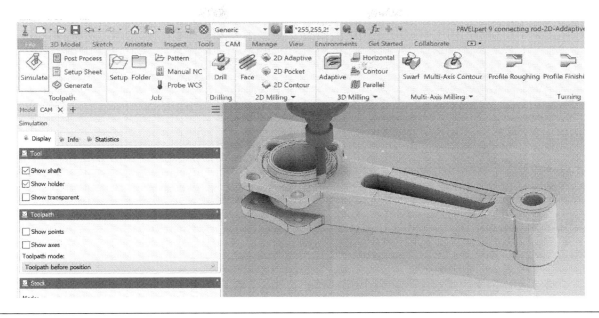

Post Processing

Now we are ready to create the CNC program. Select the operation click on the *Post Processor* on the top of the menu tab. Click on the pull-down menu and Select FANUC/Fanuc (next to Open Confi button). In the *Program name or number* slot, change the program to 1006 or the desired number. Remember the numbers and where you saved your program. Click on *Post* to save the program to the desired Folder. This time we will create all machining processes in one program. Select the *Setup1* and run the on *Post Processor*, save to new program number 1006. The program will contain two operations, facing and contour, including all tool changes.

A new window *Autodesk Edit CAM (HSM) Edit* pops up with your new program inside. If the *Backlot* is selected, the postprocessor simulation window shows on the right.

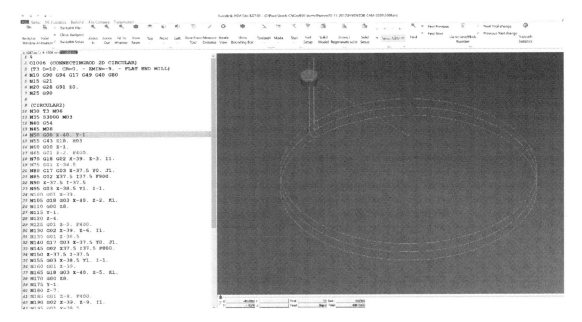

2D Contour using projection

We will use a similar setup as in the *Contour* operation describe before. If you follow the same steps, you will notice that complete contour can't be selected since the surfaces are at different levels, and some are inclined. If you want to contour the entire profile, you need to create a driving path. One of the options is to create a sketch on a plane using *Project Geometry* to project all profile edges.

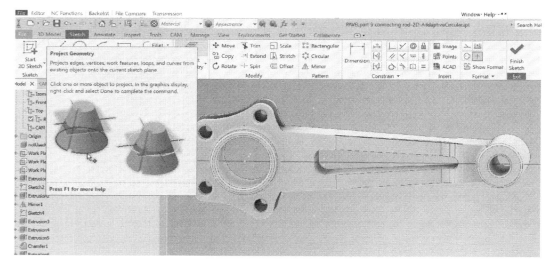

Then follow the same procedure described above for 2D *Contour*. Select *2D Contour* from the *CAM* menu, a new *2D Contour*: *2D Contour1* sub-window appears with several tabs, the first is the Tool.

We need to select a new tool from the library for contour operation. On the left side, there are *All Tools* and *Sample libraries* with submenus. Select *Sample libraries* →*Tutorial-Metric* and in the right window select tool **#4-Ø5mm** flat.

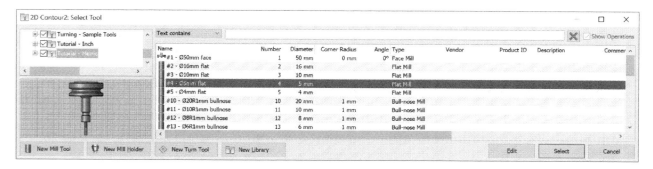

Finish it by clicking *Select* on the bottom right.

Now the tool is selected, and the number and size appear next to it *Tool: #4-Ø5mm flat.* Next to *Tool* tab select Geometry and click on edge at the bottom contour of the part; it will change the color to blue when selected.

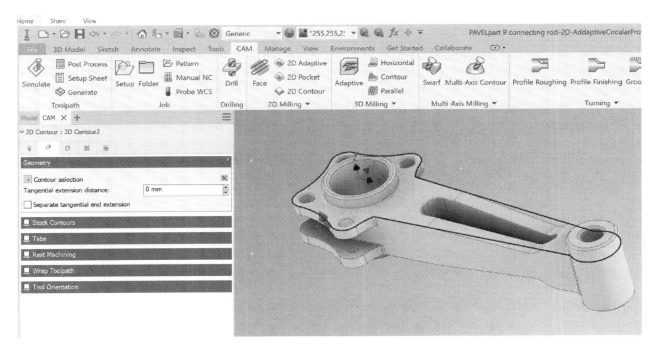

To modify the Height, select the *Bottom Height* from the menu, click on the selection and select the bottom edge of the second profile, then change *Bottom offset: -1 mm* to machine slightly bellow the bottom. The rest of the tabs Passes and Linking menus will not be modified for this part of the operation.

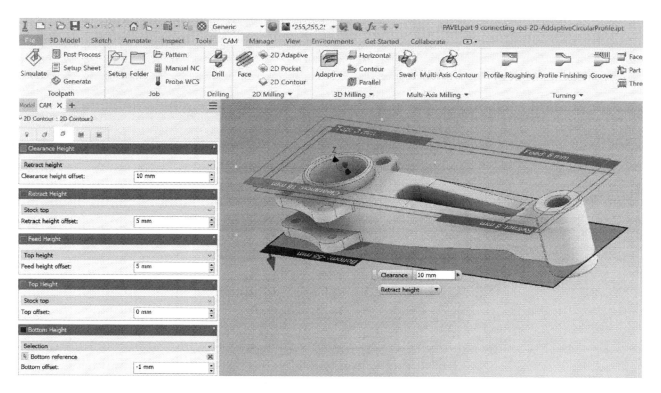

To complete the operation, click OK on the bottom of the left sub-window. Now the operation [T4]2D Contour2 is created under the previous operation as part of the Setup1. It has submenus Tool number, WCS, and size of the program in bytes. If you select [T4]2D Contour2, the tool path profile will show in the main window. Note that this process show machining at full hight of the part without stepdown and roughing operations.

Since the cutting high is too big, we will modify the contour program for multiple depths. Double click (or right-click and Edit) on the new [T4]2D Contour2, select the fourth tab, Passes, and scroll down to be able to see the Multiple Dept and check it to activate the extended menu. The first value Maximum roughing stepdown 4mm defines how much down the tool to go on each step. Unselect tthe checkbox for Stock to leave, then leave the rest of the values unchanged and click on OK to finish the modification.

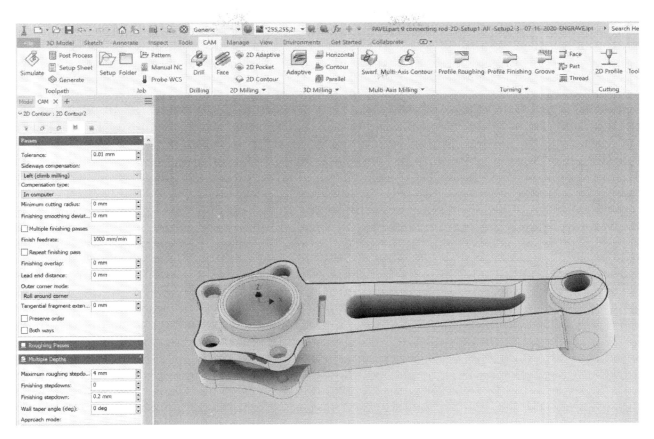

If you select [*T4*]*2D Contour2* again, the new tool path profile will show in the main window. Note that this process show machining multiple steps for the roughing operations and finishing operation.

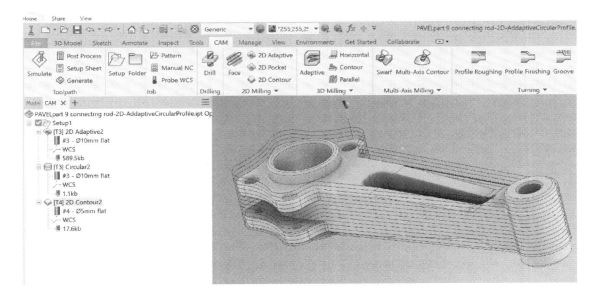

Simulation is similar to the 2D Contour process we described earlier, so we will skip the description.

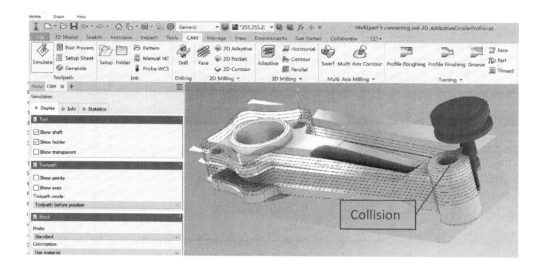

When you run the simulation, you will notice collisions between the tool holder and the workpiece. The tool and tool holder change the color to indicate the collisions.

To resolve these collision problems, increase the tool length in *[T4]2D Contour2*. Open Tool menu, select the toll #4-5mm flat, click on Edit on the bottom of the tool window, select *Cutter,* and modify values for: *Shoulder length:, Flute length:, Body length:*, and *Overall length* to desired values. Make sure you have the proper actual tool that matches these parameters, to avoid an actual collision when running this program. If you don't have the same size tool, you can change it by selecting the one you have. The program will be updated with new tool values. Rerun the simulation to very that you don't have any collisions and save the program.

Post processing

Post processing is similar to the 2D Contour process we described earlier, so here we will no skip more details.

2D Drilling and tapping

We will tap 10mm metric holes (x4) on the lower side of the Connecting rod. First, we need to create holes for tapping (1), second, enlarge the holes on the upper side (2), and finally tap the holes (3).

Drilling four holes for taps (1)

Select *Drill from* the *Drilling menu,* next to the *2D Milling* from the *CAM* menu. A new *Drill: Drill2* sub-window appears with several tabs, the first one is the Tool. Click on the Tool button.

We need to select a tool from the library. On the left side, there are *All Tools* and *Sample libraries* with submenus. Stroll down and select *Metric-Low Carbon Steel*, On the right side, select the tool **Ø8.9mm drill (118^0 drill)** that corresponds to the minor thread diameter, and finish by clicking *Select* on the bottom right. The new tool is selected, and its number and size appear next to *Tool: #1-Ø8.9mm drill.*

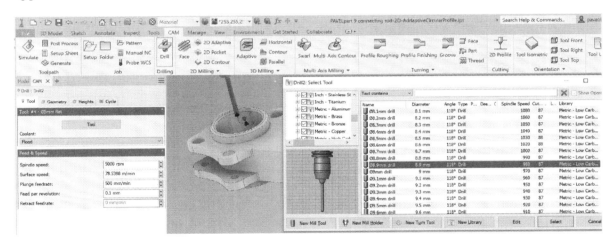

Select *Geometry* next to the *Tool* tab, click on *Hole faces*, and select the top of one of the holes with 10mm thread, it will change the color to blue when selected. Next, under Hole faces, click on *Select the same diameter*; this will select all the holes within the part with the same diameter. We need to modify the *Heights* to make sure the drill cutt throug the bottom of the hole. Select *Heights* tab and on the *Bottom Height*, select *Drill tip through bottom*, then set the *Break-through dept: 2mm*. The rest of the tabs *Height* and *Linking* menus will not be modified for this part of the operation.

Complete the operation by clicking *OK* on the bottom left side of the *Drill* sub-window. Now the operation *[T1]Drill2 [Rapid out]* is created as part of the *Setup1*. It has submenus Tool number, WCS, and size of the program in bytes.

Note that depends on the precision of the process you design; you may need to use spot drill to set up a leading hole for the drilling. The process is the same as described below, juts you need to select spot drill instead of regular drill and define appropriate *Heights*.

Simulaion

We can simulate all the *Drill2* processes by selecting *Simulate* on the main tab. A new simulation window pops up, and the control buttons are the same as described above. You can select the checkbox *Stock* and then select *Material: Show Transparent and Show Part comparison* to see stock and additional details. Click on the *Close* button and go back to the *CAM* menu. Save the Inventor file that now includes *2D Circular* CAM simulation.

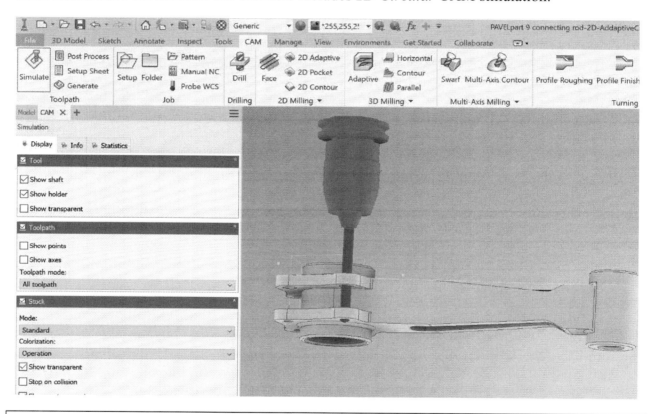

Post Processing

We will delay post processing description until we finish these holes drilling and tapping processes.

This time instead of creating a new drilling process, we will reuse the setting from existing drilling (duplicate it) and make some tool and geometry modifications.

Right-click (or Ctr+D) on *[T1]Drill2 [Rapid out]* menu and select *Duplicate*. A new *[T1]Drill2 (3)[Rapid out]*will appear under *[T1]Drill2 [Rapid out].* Click to edit it and select the *Tool* menu.

We need to select a new tool from the library. On the left side, there are *All Tools* and *Sample libraries* with submenus. Stroll down and select *Metric-Low Carbon Steel*, On the right side, select the tool **Ø13mm drill (118⁰ drill)**, and finish by clicking *Select* on the bottom right. The new tool is selected, and its number and size appear next to *Tool: #2-*Ø13mm drill.

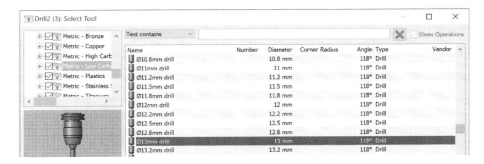

Select *Geometry* next to the *Tool* tab, click on *Hole faces,* and select the top of one of the 13mm holes on the top surface, it will change the color to blue when selected. Next, under *Hole faces,* click on *Select same diameter*; this will select all the holes within the part with same diameter.

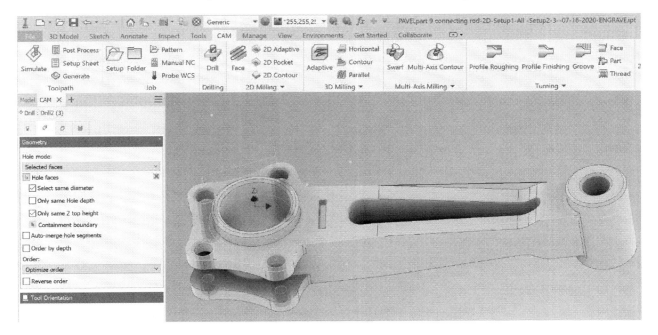

We need to modify the *Heights* to cut only throughthe top holes. Select *Heights* tab and on the *Bottom Height*, Click on the *Selection* pudown menu, select the bottom surface of the top holes set, select checkox for the *Drill tip through bottom*, and then set the *Break-throug dept: 2mm.*

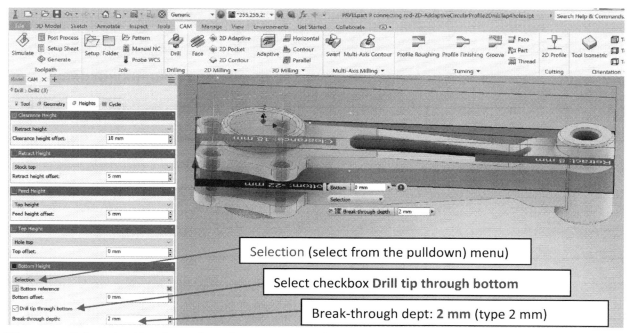

The rest of the tabs *Height* and *Linking* menus will not be modified for this part of the operation.

Complete the operation by clicking *OK* on the bottom left side of the *Drill* sub-window. Now the operation *[T1]Drill2 [Rapid out]* is created as part of the *Setup1*. It has submenus Tool number, WCS, and size of the program in bytes.

Simulation

We can simulate all the *Drill2* processes by selecting *Simulate* on the main tab. A new simulation window pops up, and the control buttons are the same as described above. You can select the checkbox *Stock* and then select *Material: Show Transparent and Show Part comparison* to see the stock and additional details. *Click* on the *Close* button and go back to the *CAM* menu. Save the Inventor file that now includes *2D Circular* CAM simulation.

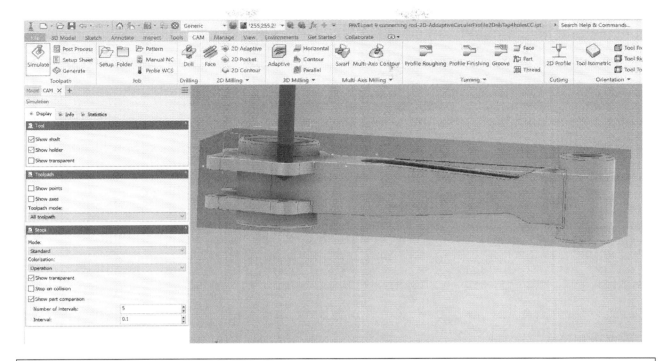

Post processing

We will delay the post processing description until we finish these holes with the tapping processes.

Tapping holes (3)

We will tap 10x1.25mm metric holes (x4) on the lower side of the Connecting rod.

Select *Drill from* the *Drilling menu,* next to the *2D Milling* from the *CAM* menu. A new *Drill: Drill5* sub-window appears with several tabs, the first one is the Tool. Click on the Tool button.

We need to select a tool from the library. On the left side, there are *All Tools* and *Sample libraries* with submenus. Stroll down and select *Taps-ISO*; on the right side, select the tool **Ø10x1.2 right tap (M10x1.5)** corresponding to the thread, and finish by clicking *Select* on the bottom right. The new tool is selected, and its number and size appear next to *Tool: #5-Ø10x1.25mm right tap (M10x1.25).*

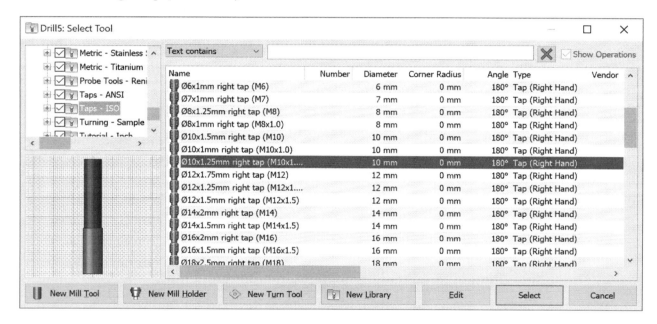

Select *Geometry* next to the *Tool* tab, click on *Hole faces,* and select the top of one of the holes with 10mm thread, it will change the color to blue when selected. Next, under Hole faces, click on *Select same diameter*; this will select all the holes within the part with the same diameter.

We need to modify the *Heights* to make sure the tap goes through the bottom of the hole. Select *Heights* tab and on the *Bottom Height*, select *Drill tip through bottom*, then set the *Break-through dept: 2mm*. The rest of the tabs *Height* and *Linking* menus will not be modified for this part of the operation.

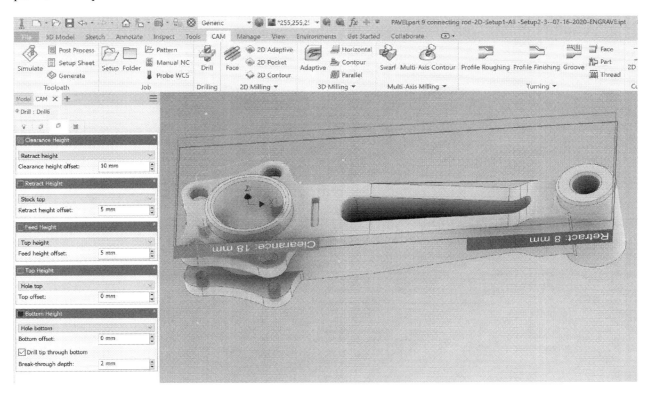

Complete the operation by clicking *OK* on the bottom left side of the *Drill* sub-window. Now the operation *[T5]: Drill6 [Tap]* is created as part of the *Setup1*. It has submenus Tool number, WCS, and size of the program in bytes.

Simulation

We can simulate all the *Drill6 [Tap]* processes by selecting *Simulate* on the main tab. A new simulation window pops up, and the control buttons are the same as described above. You can select the checkbox *Stock* and then choose *Material: Show Transparent and Show Part comparison* to see stock and additional details. *Click* on the *Close* button and go back to the *CAM* menu. Save the Inventor file that now includes *2D Circular* CAM simulation.

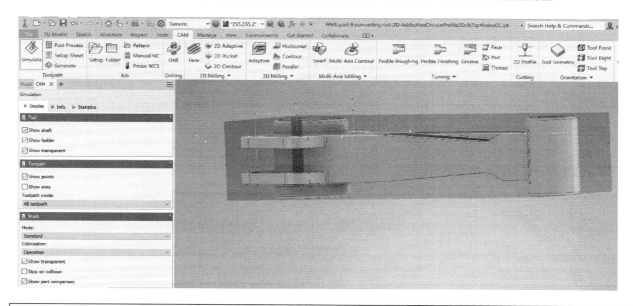

Post Processing

Now we are ready to create the complete CNC program that includes all three operations for tapping. Select the two drilling and tapping operations, then click on the *Post Processor* on the top of the menu tab. Click on the pull-down menu and Select FANUC/Fanuc (next to Open Confi button). In the *Program name or number* slot, change the program to 1007 or the desired number. Remember the numbers and where you saved your program. Click on *Post* to save the program to the desired Folder. This time we will create all machining processes in one program. Select the *Setup1* and run the on *Post Processor*, save to new program number 1007. The program will contain three operations, drilling, enlarging top holes, and tapping, including all tool changes.

A new window *Autodesk Edit CAM (HSM) Edit* pops up with your new program inside. If the *Backlot* is selected, the postprocessor simulation window shows on the right.

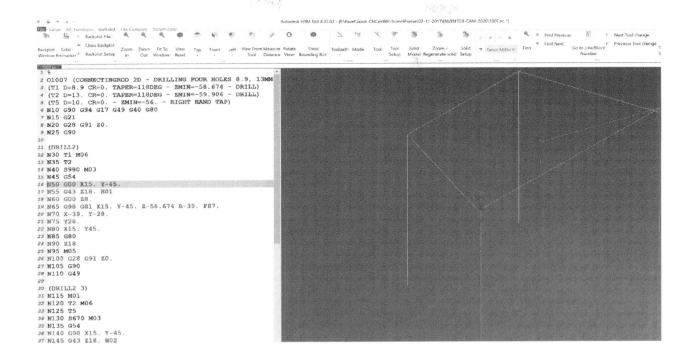

```
 1  %
 2  O1007 (CONNECTINGROD 2D - DRILLING FOUR HOLES 8.9, 13MM
 3  (T1 D=8.9 CR=0. TAPER=118DEG - ZMIN=-58.674 - DRILL)
 4  (T2 D=13. CR=0. TAPER=118DEG - ZMIN=-59.906 - DRILL)
 5  (T5 D=10. CR=0. - ZMIN=-56. - RIGHT HAND TAP)
 6  N10 G90 G94 G17 G49 G40 G80
 7  N15 G21
 8  N20 G28 G91 Z0.
 9  N25 G90
10
11  (DRILL2)
12  N30 T1 M06
13  N35 T2
14  N40 S980 M03
15  N45 G54
16  N50 G00 X15. Y-45.
17  N55 G43 Z18. H01
18  N60 G00 Z8.
19  N65 G98 G81 X15. Y-45. Z-58.674 R-39. F87.
20  N70 X-39. Y-28.
21  N75 Y28.
22  N80 X15. Y45.
23  N85 G80
24  N90 Z18.
25  N95 M05
26  N100 G28 G91 Z0.
27  N105 G90
28  N110 G49
29
30  (DRILL2 3)
31  N115 M01
32  N120 T2 M06
33  N125 T5
34  N130 S670 M03
35  N135 G54
36  N140 G00 X15. Y-45.
37  N145 G43 Z18. H02
```

133

2D Slot

From the *CAM* menu select *2D* Milling pulldown menu and select *Slot*, a new sub-window appears with several tabs, the first one is the Tool. Click on the Tool button.

We need to select a tool from the library. On the left side, there are *All Tools* and *Sample libraries* with submenus. On the right side, select the same tool **#4-Ø5mm flat (5mm flat mill)**, we used it in one of the previous processes, and finish the operation by clicking *Select* on the bottom right. The tool is selected, and its number and size appear next to *Tool: #4-Ø5mm flat.*

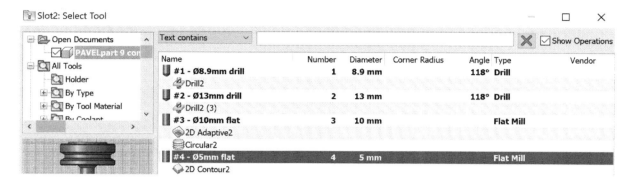

Select *Geometry* next to the *Tool* tab, click on *Pocket selections,* and select the top outside of the slot; it will change the color to blue when selected. This machining operation will machine the slot with the width equal to the tool size.

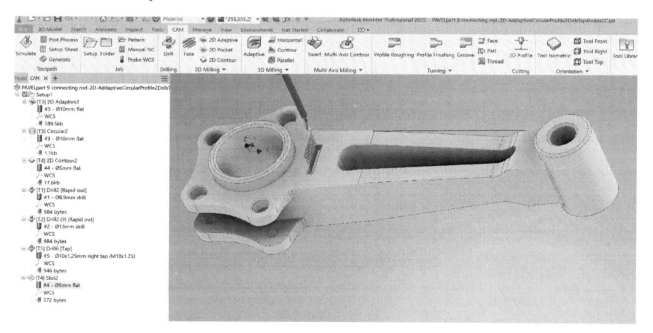

The rest of the tabs *Height*, *Passes*, and *Linking* menus will not be modified for this part of the operation. More detail for each tab will be given later with other operations.

Complete the operation by clicking *OK* on the bottom left side of the sub-window. Now the operation *[T4]Slot2* is created as part of the *Setup1*. It has submenus Tool number, WCS, and size of the program in bytes. If you select *[T4]Slot2,* the tool paths will show on the main window. Note that this process is machining from the top of the stock, with zigzag steps, until the full depth is reached.

Simulation

We can simulate all the *2D Circular* processes by selecting *Simulate* on the main tab. A new simulation window pops up, and the control buttons are the same as described above. You can select the checkbox *Stock* and then choose *Material: Show Transparent and Show Part comparison* to see stock and additional details. *Click* on the *Close* button and go back to the *CAM* menu. Save the Inventor file that now includes *[T4]Slot2* simulation.

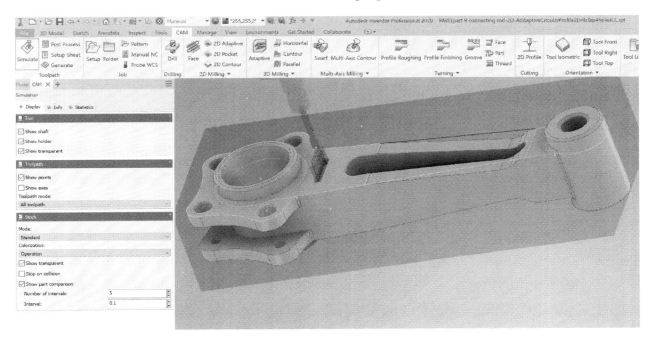

Post Processing

We will delay the post processing description and show it after finishing the machining of the big cylinder hole.

2D Bore

From the *CAM* menu select *2D* Milling pulldown menu and select *Bore*, a new sub-window appears with several tabs, the first one is the Tool. Click on the Tool button.

We need to select a tool from the library. On the left side, there are *All Tools* and *Sample libraries* with submenus. On the right side, select the same tool **#4-Ø10mm flat (10mm flat mill)** used in one of the previous processes, and finish the process by clicking *Select* on the bottom right. The tool is selected, and its number and size appear next to *Tool: #4-*Ø10mm flat.

Select *Geometry* next to the *Tool* tab, click on *Circular face selection* and select the inside surface of the big cylinder hole; it will change the color to blue when selected.

The rest of the tabs *Height*, *Passes*, and *Linking* menus will not be modified for this part of the operation. More detail for each tab will be given later with other operations.

Complete the operation by clicking *OK* on the bottom left side of the sub-window. Now the operation *[T3]Bore2* is created as part of the *Setup1*. It has submenus Tool number, WCS, and size of the program in bytes. If you select *[T4]Slot2*, the tool paths will show on the main window.

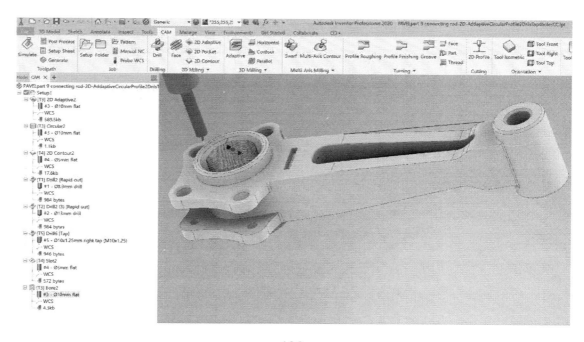

Note that this process is machining from the top of the stock, with spiral down steps, until the full depth is reached.

Simulation

We can simulate all the *[T3]Bore2* processes by selecting *Simulate* on the main tab.

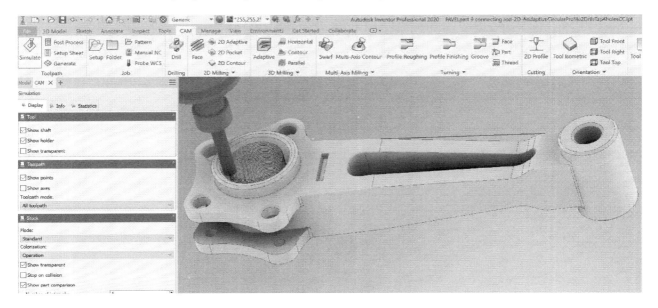

Post Processing

Now we will create one CNC program for the slot and the bore operation. Select the operations *Slot* and *Bore2*, then click on the *Post Processor* on the top of the menu tab. Click on the pull-down menu and Select FANUC/Fanuc (next to Open Confi button). In the *Program name or number* slot, change the program to 1008 or the desired number. Remember the numbers and where you saved your program. Click on *Post* to save the program to the desired Folder. This time we will create all machining processes in one program. Select the *Setup1* and run the on *Post Processor*, save to new program number 1008. The program will contain two operations, facing and contour, including all tool changes.

A new window *Autodesk Edit CAM (HSM) Edit* pops up with your new program inside. If the *Backlot* is selected, the postprocessor simulation window shows on the right.

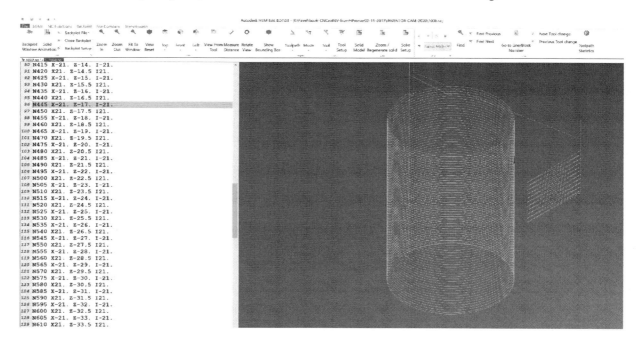

2D Chamfer

From the *CAM* menu select *2D* Milling pulldown menu and select 2D Chafer, a new sub-window appears with several tabs, the first one is the Tool. Click on the *Tool* button. This time we will use metric tools.

We need to select a tool from the library. On the left side, there are *All Tools* and *Sample libraries* with submenus select Tutorial-Metric. On the right side, select the tool **#50-Ø10mm 45⁰** and finish by clicking *Select* on the bottom right. The new tool is selected, and its number and size appear next to *Tool:* **#50-Ø10mm 45⁰ chamfer.**

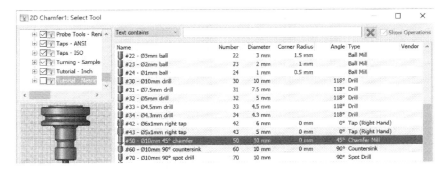

Select *Geometry* next to the *Tool* tab, click on *Contour selection,* and select the bottom side of inside and outside chamfer of the big cylinder; it will change the color to blue when selected. Click on the *Passes* and change *Chamfer tip offset: 1 mm*. We need to offset the tool a bit down to make sure it machines with its side.

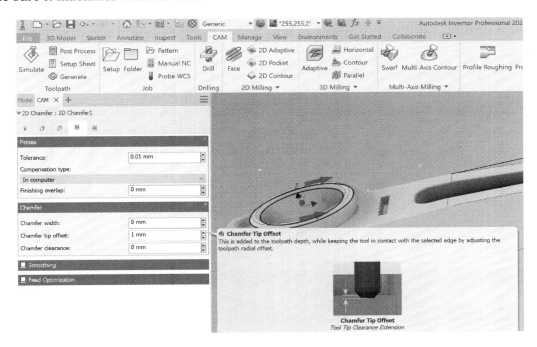

The rest of the tabs *Height* and *Linking* menus will not be modified for this part of the operation. More detail for each tab will be given later with other operations.

Complete the operation by clicking *OK* on the bottom left side of the sub-window. Now the operation *[T50]2D Chamfer1* is created as part of the *Setup1*. It has submenus Tool number, WCS, and size of the program in bytes. If you select *#50-Ø10mm 45⁰ chamfer,* the tool paths will show on the main window.

Simulation

We can simulate all the *[T50]2D Chamfer1* processes by selecting *Simulate* on the main tab.

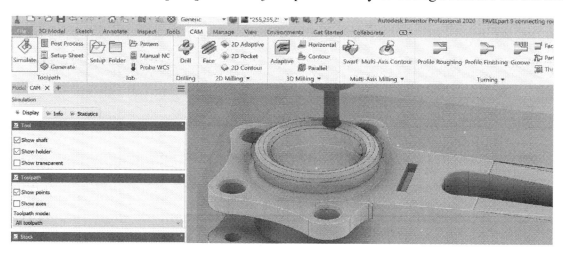

Post Processing

Now we are ready to create the next CNC program. Select the operation click on the *Post Processor* on the top of the menu tab. Click on the pull-down menu and Select FANUC/Fanuc (next to Open Confi button). In the *Program name or number* slot, change the program to 1009 or the desired number. Select the *Setup1* and run the on *Post Processor*, save to new program number 1009. The program will contain two chamfer operations.

A new window *Autodesk Edit CAM (HSM) Edit* pops up with your new program inside. If the *Backlot* is selected, the postprocessor simulation window shows on the right.

```
1 %
2 O1009 (CONNECTINGROD 2D - MACHINING-2 CHAMFERS ON THE B
3 (T50 D=10. CR=0. TAPER=45DEG - ZMIN=-1. - CHAMFER MILL)
4 N10 G90 G94 G17 G49 G40 G80
5 N15 G21
6 N20 G28 G91 Z0.
7 N25 G90
8
9 (2D CHAMFER1)
10 N30 T50 M06
11 N35 S5000 M03
12 N40 G54
13 N45 M08
14 N50 G00 X22.993 Y0.564
15 N55 G43 Z18. H50
16 N60 G00 Z8.
17 N65 G01 Z5. F500.
18 N70 Z-1.
19 N75 X23.993 Y0.589
20 N80 G03 X-23.993 Y-0.589 I-23.993 J-0.589 F1000.
21 N85 X23.993 Y0.589 I23.993 J0.589
22 N90 G01 X22.993 Y0.564
23 N95 G00 Z8.
24 N100 X35.5 Y0.
25 N105 G01 Z5. F500.
26 N110 Z-1.
27 N115 X34.5
28 N120 G02 X-34.5 I-34.5 F1000.
29 N125 X34.5 I34.5
30 N130 G01 X35.5
31 N135 G00 Z18.
32
33 N140 M09
34 N145 G28 G91 Z0.
35 N150 G90
36 N155 G49
37 N160 G28 G91 X0. Y0.
38 N165 G90
39 N170 M30
40 %
41
```

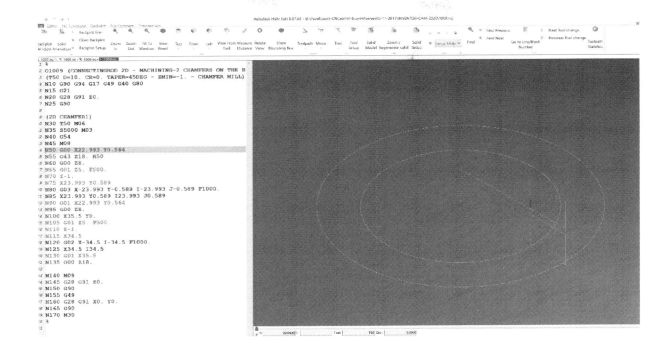

2D Trace

From the *CAM* menu select *2D* Milling pulldown menu and select Trace, a new sub-window appears with several tabs, the first one is the Tool. Click on the Tool button. This time we will use metric tools.

We need to select a tool from the library that matches the fillet radius. On the left side, there are *All Tools* and *Sample libraries* with submenus select Tutorial-Metric. On the right side, select the tool **#21-Ø6mm ball** and finish by clicking *Select* on the bottom right. The new tool is selected, and its number and size appear next to *Tool:* **#6-Ø6mm ball.**

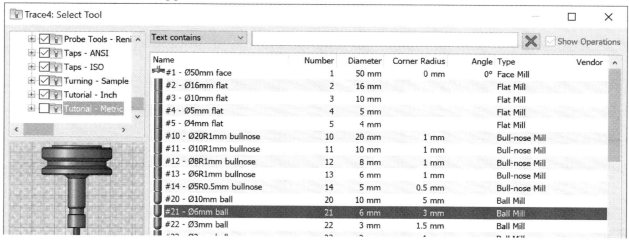

Select *Geometry* next to the *Tool* tab, click on *Curve selection,* and select the bottom side of the outside round fillet of the big cylinder; it will change the color to blue when selected.

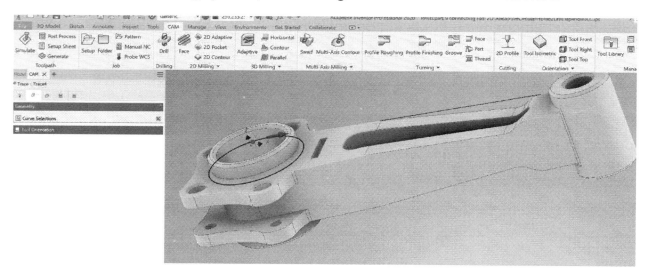

The rest of the tabs *Height, Passes,* and *Linking* menus will not be modified for this part of the operation. More detail for each tab will be given later with other operations.

Complete the operation by clicking *OK* on the bottom left side of the sub-window. Now the operation *[T21]Trace4* is created as part of the *Setup1*. It has submenus Tool number, WCS, and size of the program in bytes. If you select *#21 – 6mm ball,* the tool paths will show on the main window.

Simulation

We can simulate all the *[T21]Trace4* processes by selecting *Simulate* on the main tab.

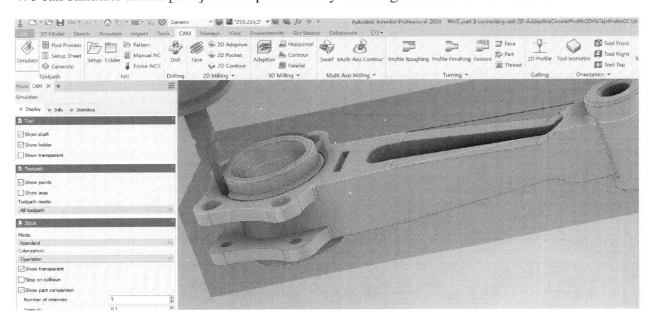

Post Processing

Now we are ready to create the next CNC program. Select the operation click on the *Post Processor* on the top of the menu tab. Click on the pull-down menu and Select FANUC/Fanuc (next to Open Confi button). In the *Program name or number* slot, change the program to 1010 or the desired number. Select the *Setup1* and run the on *Post Processor*, save to new program number 1010. The program will contain two chamfer operations.

A new window *Autodesk Edit CAM (HSM) Edit* pops up with your new program inside. If the *Backlot* is selected, the postprocessor simulation window shows on the right.

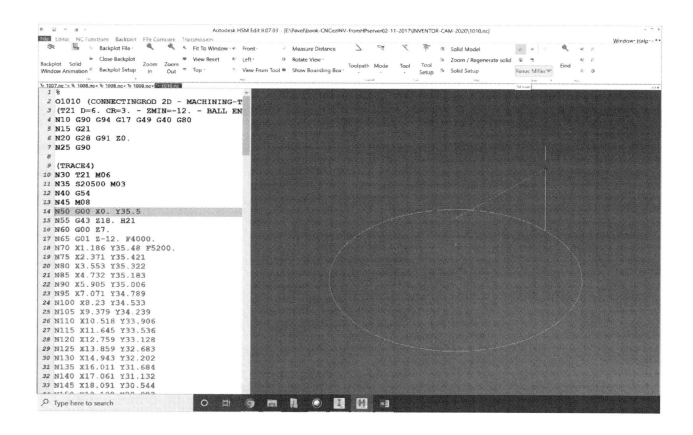

```
 1  %
 2  O1010 (CONNECTINGROD 2D - MACHINING-T
 3  (T21 D=6. CR=3. - ZMIN=-12. - BALL EN
 4  N10 G90 G94 G17 G49 G40 G80
 5  N15 G21
 6  N20 G28 G91 Z0.
 7  N25 G90
 8
 9  (TRACE4)
10  N30 T21 M06
11  N35 S20500 M03
12  N40 G54
13  N45 M08
14  N50 G00 X0. Y35.5
15  N55 G43 Z18. H21
16  N60 G00 Z7.
17  N65 G01 Z-12. F4000.
18  N70 X1.186 Y35.48 F5200.
19  N75 X2.371 Y35.421
20  N80 X3.553 Y35.322
21  N85 X4.732 Y35.183
22  N90 X5.905 Y35.006
23  N95 X7.071 Y34.789
24  N100 X8.23 Y34.533
25  N105 X9.379 Y34.239
26  N110 X10.518 Y33.906
27  N115 X11.645 Y33.536
28  N120 X12.759 Y33.128
29  N125 X13.859 Y32.683
30  N130 X14.943 Y32.202
31  N135 X16.011 Y31.684
32  N140 X17.061 Y31.132
33  N145 X18.091 Y30.544
```

Drilling and tapping the small cylinder hole M12x2.5mm

We will tap M20x2.5 mm metric hole in the smaller cylinder of the Connecting rod part. First, we need to create holes for tapping (1) then we can tap the hole (2).

Drilling small cylinder hole (1)

Again, instead of creating a new drilling process, we will reuse the setting from existing drilling (duplicate it) and make some tool and geometry modifications.

Right-click on *[T2]Drill2 (3) [Rapid out]* menu and select *Duplicate* (or use Ctr+D). A new *[T1]Drill2 (4)[Rapid out]*will appear under *[T2]Drill2 (3)[Rapid out]*. You can click on in and drag it down to make it the last of all processes. After duplicating the process, double click on it to edit it and select the *Tool* menu.

We need to select a tool from the library for drilling the hole before tapping it. On the left side, there are *All Tools* and *Sample libraries* with submenus. Stroll down and select *Metric-Low Carbon Steel*, On the right side, select the tool **Ø17.5mm drill (118⁰ drill)**, and finish by clicking *Select* on the bottom right. The new tool is selected, and its number and size appear next to *Tool: #6-Ø17.5mm drill*.

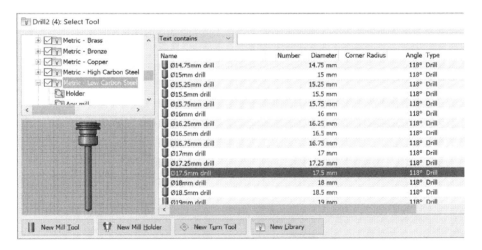

Select *Geometry* next to the *Tool* tab, click on *Hole faces,* and select the M20x2.5mm thread hole; it will change the color to blue when selected. Next, under *Hole faces*, click on uncheck the box for *Select same diameter*. We need to modify the *Heights* to cut through the hole. Select *Heights* tab and on the *Bottom Height*, Click on the *Selection* pulldown menu, then select *Drill tip through bottom*, then set the *Break-through dept: 2mm* and select the bottom surface of the hole.

The rest of the tabs *Height* and *Linking* menus will not be modified for this part of the operation.

Complete the operation by clicking *OK* on the bottom left side of the *Drill* sub-window. Now the operation *[6] Drill2 [Rapid out]* is created as part of the *Setup1*. It has submenus Tool number, WCS, and size of the program in bytes.

Note that depends on the precision of the process you design; you may need to use spot drill to set up a leading hole for the drilling. The process is the same as described below, juts you need to select spot drilling instead of the regular one and define appropriate *Heights*. Further, if the hole size is large, you need to predrill the pilot hole with a small size drill and then enlarge it with a bigger size drill. In case that the hole is larger than the drilling tool you have, bore operation can use instead.

Simulation

We can simulate all the *Drill2* processes by selecting *Simulate* on the main tab. A new simulation window pops up, and the control buttons are the same as described above. You can select the checkbox *Stock* and then select *Material: Show Transparent and Show Part comparison* to see stock and additional details. *Click* on the *Close* button and go back to the *CAM* menu.

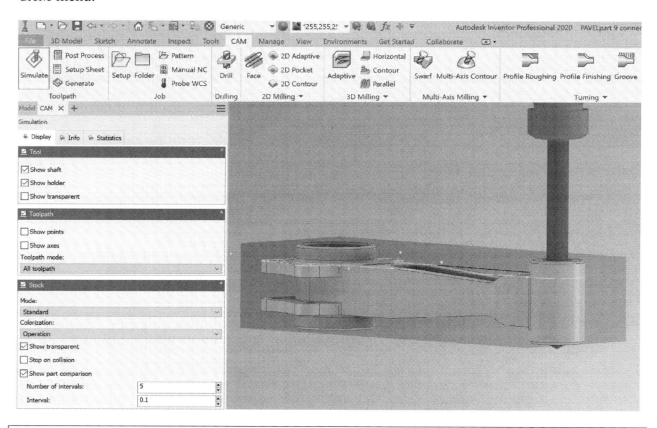

Post Processing

We will delay post processing description and show after we finish the threading process.

Tapping small cylinder hole (2)

Again, instead of creating a new tapping process, we will reuse the setting from existing tapping (duplicate it) and make some tool and geometry modifications.

Right-click on *[T5]Drill6 [Tap]* menu and select *Duplicate* (or use Ctr+D). A new *[T5]Drill6 (2)[Tap]* will appear under *[T5]Drill6 [Tap]*. You can click on in and drag it down to be the last of the processes. After duplicating the tapping process, double click on it to edit it and select the *Tool* menu.

We need to select a tool from the library. On the left side, there are *All Tools* and *Sample libraries* with submenus. Stroll down and select *Taps-ISO*, On the right side, select the tool **Ø20mm right tap (M20)**, and finish by clicking *Select* on the bottom right. The new tool is selected, and its number and size appear next to **Tool: #7-Ø20mm right tap (M20)**

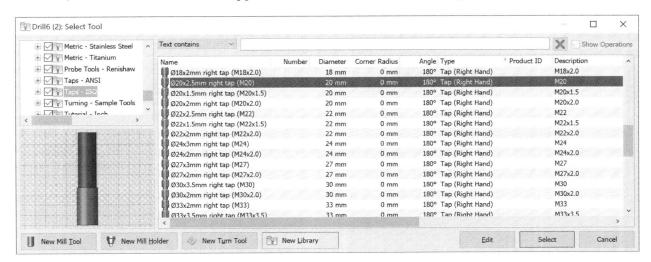

Select *Geometry* next to the *Tool* tab, click on *Hole faces,* and select the M20x2.5mm thread hole;it will change the color to blue when selected. Next, under *Hole faces*, click on uncheck the box for *Select same diameter*. We need to modify the *Heights* to cut only through the top holes. Select *Heights* tab and on the *Bottom Height*, Click on the *Selection* pulldown menu, then select *Drill tip through bottom*, then set the *Break- through depth: 3mm*.

The rest of the tabs *Height* and *Linking* menus will not be modified for this part of the operation.

Complete the operation by clicking *OK* on the bottom left side of the *Drill* sub-window. Now the operation *[T5]Drill6 (2)[Tap]* is created as part of the *Setup1*. It has submenus Tool number, WCS, and size of the program in bytes.

In some cases, when the tap size is larger than the tap tool you have, milling threading operation can use instead.

We can simulate all the *Tap* processes by selecting *Simulate* on the main tab. A new simulation window pops up, and the control buttons are the same as described above. You can select the checkbox *Stock* and then select *Material: Show Transparent and Show Part comparison* to see stock and additional details. *Click* on the *Close* button and go back to the *CAM* menu.

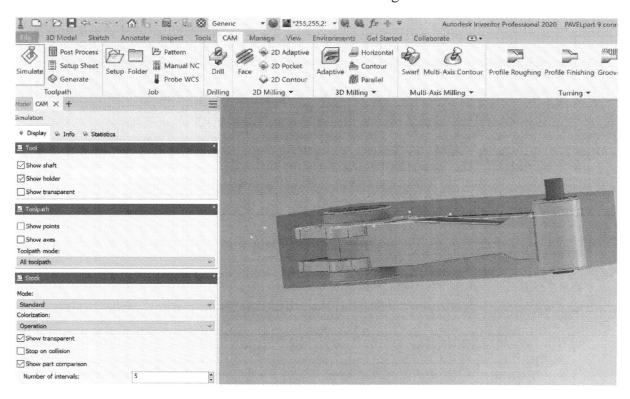

Now we are ready to create the CNC program for the drilling and tapping operations. Select the drilling and tapping operations *for M20x2.5mm* click on the *Post Processor* on the top of the menu tab. Click on the pull-down menu and Select FANUC/Fanuc (next to Open Confi button). In the *Program name or number* slot, change the program to 1011 or the desired number. Select the *Setup1* and run the on *Post Processor*, save to new program number 1011. The program will contain drilling and tapping operations *M20x2.5mm*.

A new window *Autodesk Edit CAM (HSM) Edit* pops up with your new program inside. If the *Backlot* is selected, the postprocessor simulation window shows on the right.

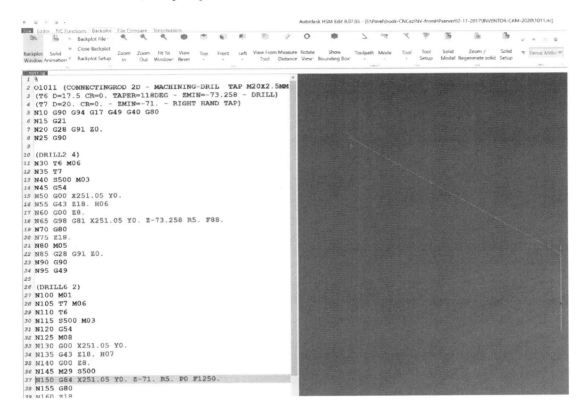

2D Pocket

From the *CAM* menu select *2D* Pocket, a new sub-window appears with several tabs; the first one is the *Tool*. Click on the *Tool* button.

We need to select a tool from the library. On the left side, there are *All Tools* and *Sample libraries* with submenus. On the right side, select the same tool **#4-Ø5mm flat (5mm flat mill)** we used in one of the previous processes and finish by clicking *Select* on the bottom right. The tool is selected, and its number and size appear next to *Tool: #4-Ø5mm flat.*

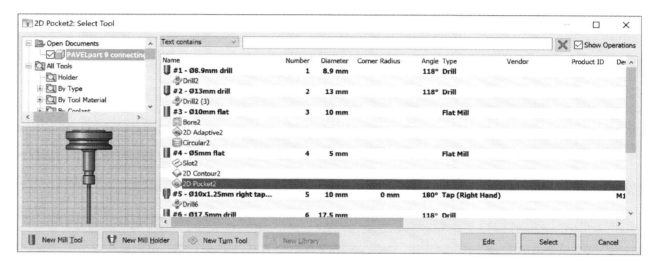

Select *Geometry* next to the *Tool* tab, click on *Pocke selections,* and select the bottom outline of the big middle slot, it will change the color to blue when selected. Select *Passes* tab, click on *Multiple Depths*, modify *Maximum roughing stepdown*: *2 mm*, then bellow uncheck the box for *Stock to Leave.*

The rest of the tabs *Height* and *Linking* menus will not be modified for this part of the operation. More detail for each tab will be given later with other operations. Let Complete the Finish the operation by clicking *OK* on the bottom left side of the sub-window. Now the operation *[T4] 2D Pocket2* is created as part of the *Setup1*. It has submenus Tool number, WCS, and size of the program in bytes. Note that this process is machining from the top of the stock, with steps (including spiral down steps), until the full depth is reached.

Simulation

We can simulate all the *2D Circular* processes by selecting *Simulate* on the main tab. A new simulation window pops up, and the control buttons are the same as described above. You can select the checkbox *Stock* and then choose *Material: Show Transparent and Show Part comparison* to see stock and additional details. *Click* on the *Close* button and go back to the *CAM* menu. Save the Inventor file that now includes *T4] 2D Pocket2* simulation.

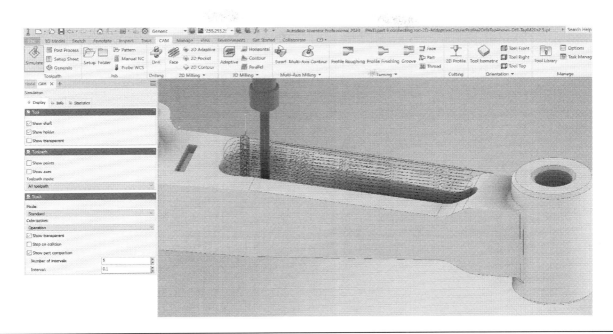

Post Processing

Now we are ready to create the next CNC program. Select the operation click on the *Post Processor* on the top of the menu tab. Click on the pull-down menu and Select FANUC/Fanuc (next to Open Confi button). In the *Program name or number* slot, change the program to 1012 or the desired number and seave it.

A new window *Autodesk Edit CAM (HSM) Edit* pops up with your new program inside. If the *Backlot* is selected, the postprocessor simulation window shows on the right.

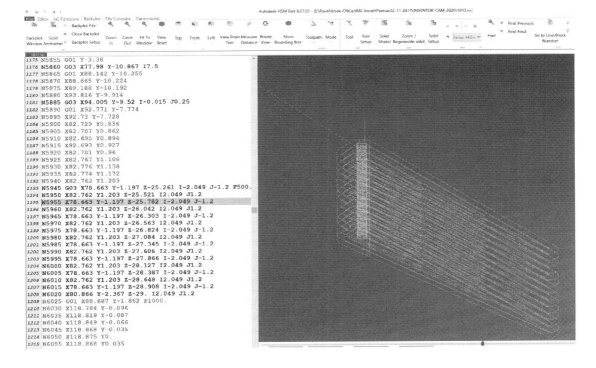

Simulation of all operations on Setup1

We can simulate all machining operations by selecting *Setup1,* then selecting *Simulate* on the main tab. A new simulation window pops up, and the control buttons are the same as described above. You can select the checkbox *Stock* and then choose *Material: Show Transparent and Show Part comparison* to see stock and additional details. *Click* on the *Close* button and go back to the *CAM* menu. Save the Inventor file that now includes *Seuep1* simulation, including all processes.

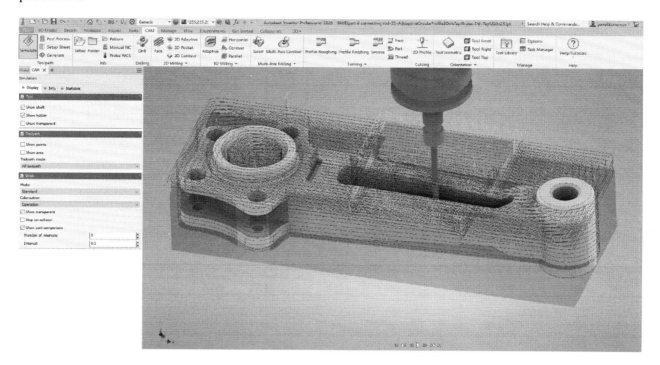

Post Processing all operation on Setup1

Now we are ready to create the CNC program with multiple operations. Select the *Setup1,* click on the *Post Processor* on the top of the menu tab. Click on the pull-down menu and Select FANUC/Fanuc (next to Open Confi button). In the *Program name or number* slot, change the program to 1013 or the desired number. Select the *Setup1* and run the on *Post Processor*, save to new program number 1013. The program will contain all operations listed under *Setup1,* includng tool changes. At the begging of the program, all tools and their sizes are listed.

A new window *Autodesk Edit CAM (HSM) Edit* pops up with your new program inside. If the *Backlot* is selected, the postprocessor simulation window shows on the right.

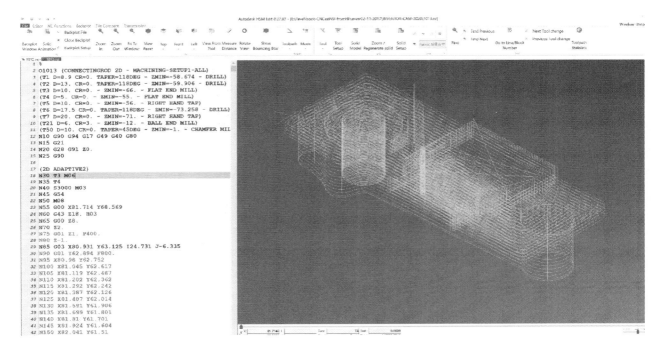

2D Engrave

Finally, we will create one additional operation in 2D milling used to engrave contours of letters, numbers, and 2D figures. Engrave is machining contour with V shaped tool. Before using the 2D contour need to be created. Create a new sketch plane and create the desired contour. You can also use the *Text* tool to create a text.

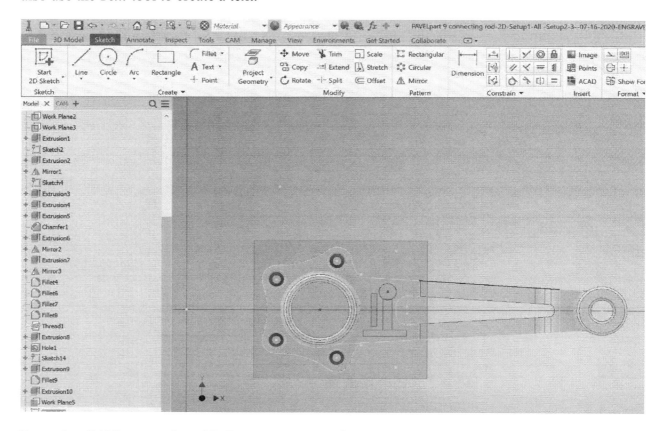

From the *CAM* menu select *2D Engrave*, a new sub-window appears with several tabs, the first one is the *Tool*. Click on the *Tool* button.

We need to select a tool from the library. On the left side, there are *All Tools* and *Sample libraries* with submenus. On the right side, select the same tool **#50-Ø10mm 45⁰ chamfer (10mm 45⁰ chamfer mill)** we used in one of the previous processes and finish by clicking *Select* on the bottom right. The tool is selected, and its number and size appear next to *Tool: #50-Ø10mm 45⁰ chamfer.*

Select *Geometry* next to the *Tool* tab, click on *Contour Selection* and select all countours from the sketch, it will change the color to blue when selected. The rest of the tabs *Height, Passes,* and *Linking* menus will not be modified for this part of the operation.

Let Complete the operation by clicking *OK* on the bottom left side of the sub-window. Now the operation *[T50] Engrave2* is created as part of the *Setup1*. It has submenus Tool number, WCS, and size of the program in bytes. If you select *#50-Ø10mm 45⁰ chamfer,* the tool paths will show on the main window.

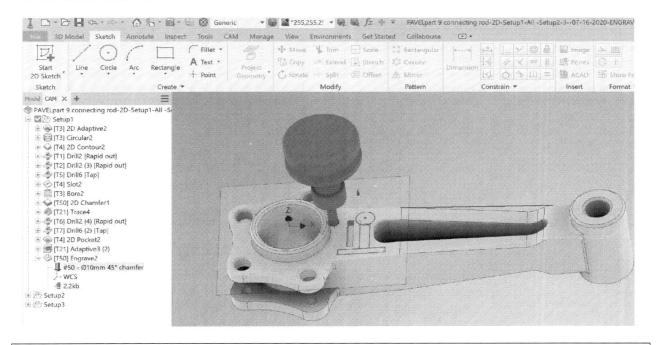

Simulation

We can simulate the *Engrave2* processes by selecting *Simulate* on the main tab. A new simulation window pops up, and the control buttons are the same as described above. You can select the checkbox *Stock* and then select *Material: Show Transparent and Show Part comparison* to see stock and additional details. *Click* on the *Close* button and go back to the *CAM* menu. Save the Inventor file that now includes *Engrave2* simulation.

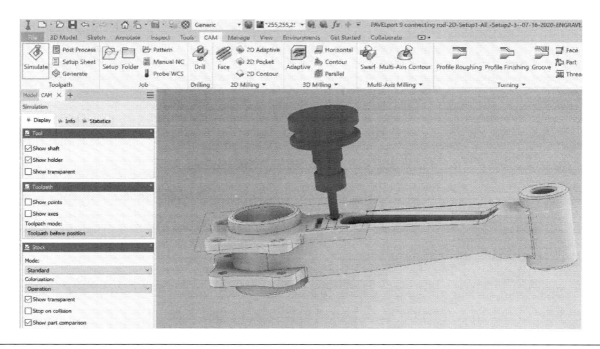

Now we are ready to create the next CNC program. Select the operation click on the *Post Processor* on the top of the menu tab. Click on the pull-down menu and Select FANUC/Fanuc (next to Open Confi button). In the *Program name or number* slot, change the program to 1014 or desired number. Select the *Setup1* and run the on *Post Processor*, save to new program number 1014.

A new window *Autodesk Edit CAM (HSM) Edit* pops up with your new program inside. If the *Backlot* is selected, the postprocessor simulation window shows on the right.

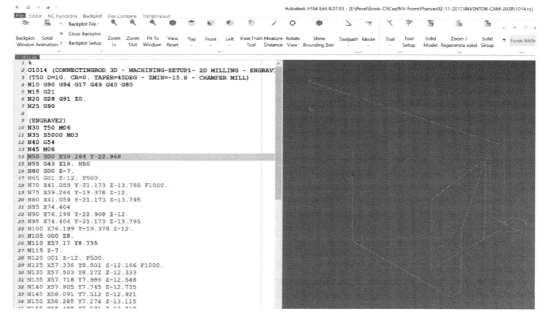

2D machining using Setup2

We machined all the surfaces from the top of the part using Setup1, now we will machine the bottom side by using separate *Setup2*. Again we will begin by defining the stock and the origin of the part to be machined.

Setup2

Click on *Setup* menu; we will use the same *Stock* from *Setup1*. Next, select *the Setup2* tab to change the position of the coordinate system. Flip the part, rotate 180^0 degrees so the bottom from *Setup1* is now facing up.

Origin: select *Point* and click on a point on the part (e.g., top-left cylinder). The origin will move to that point, if the orientations of X, Y Z axis are not on the desired direction, use *Orientation:* to revert to the desired direction. For this setup example, all the coordinates in machining will be referenced from this origin. If you need to rotate or move the part to a new position(s), you can create a new setup(s) for that position(s). Finish the Setup, click OK, a new *CAM* tab is created next to the *Model* tab.

The next step is creating the tool paths using *2D Milling*, *3D Milling,* or *Turning*. We will start *Setup2* machining with a *2D Adaptive* operation, a part of *2D Milling*.

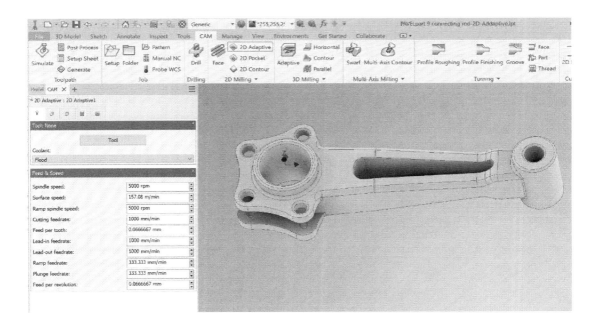

Select *2D Adaptive* from the *CAM* menu, a new *2D Adaptive: 2D Adaptive* sub-window appears with several tabs; the first one is the Tool. Click on the Tool button. This time we will use metric tools.

We need to select a tool from the library. On the left side, there are *All Tools* and *Sample library* with submenus. Select *Sample Library→Tutorial-Metric (or other)*, then on the right window select tool **#2-Ø16mm flat (16mm flat mill)** and finish by clicking *Select* on the bottom right. The new tool is selected, and its number and size appear next to *Tool: #2-Ø*16mm flat.

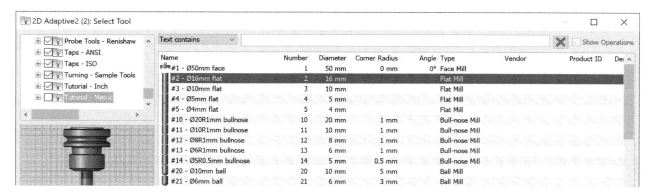

Select *Geometry* next to the *Tool* tab, click on the *Pocket selection,* and select the top left flat surface; it will change the color to blue when selected. You can select multiple 2D pockets, let select the right cylinder top and flat surface next to it. This machining operation will only machine flat type of surfaces. Later we will discuss how to machine *3D Adaptive* surfaces.

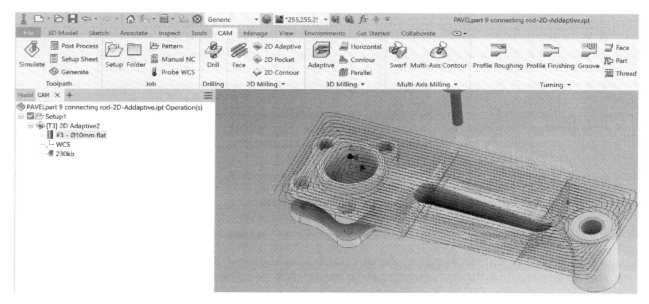

The rest of the tabs *Height*, *Passes*, and *Linking* menus will not be modified for this part of the operation. More detail for each tab will be given later with other operations.

Compete the operation by clicking *OK* on the bottom left side of the 2D Adaptive sub-window. Now the operation *[T3]2D Adaptive2* (2) is created as part of the *Setup1*. It has submenus Tool number, WCS, and size of the program in bytes. If you select *[T3]2D Adaptive2 (2),* the tool paths will show on the main window. Note that this process is machining at the full hight on the flat surfaces we selected to the top surfaces of the part. Here we assume that pocket is machined from a solid material. We will modify the program for multiple depths.

Double click (or right-click and Edit) on the new *[T2]2D Adaptive2 (2)* menu, select the fourth tab, *Passes* and scroll down to see the *Multiple Dept* and check it to activate the extented menu. Change the *Maximum roughing stepdown: 3mm* and unselect *Stock to leave*. Leave the rest of the parameters unchanged and click on *OK* to finish the modification. If you select *[T2]2D Adaptive2 (2)* again, the tool path profile will show in the main window. Note that this process show machining of pockets with multiple steps.

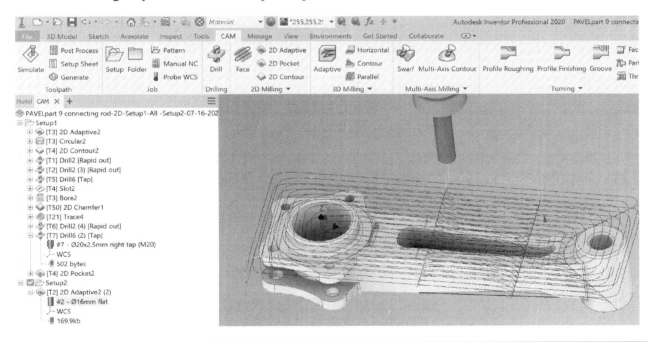

Simulation

We can simulate all the *2D Adaptive* processes by selecting *Simulate* on the main tab. A new simulation window pops up, and the control buttons are the same as described above. You can select the checkbox *Stock* and then choose *Material: Show Transparent and Show Part comparison* to see stock and additional details. Click on the *Close* button and go back to the *CAM* menu. Save the Inventor file that now includes *2D Adaptive* CAM simulation.

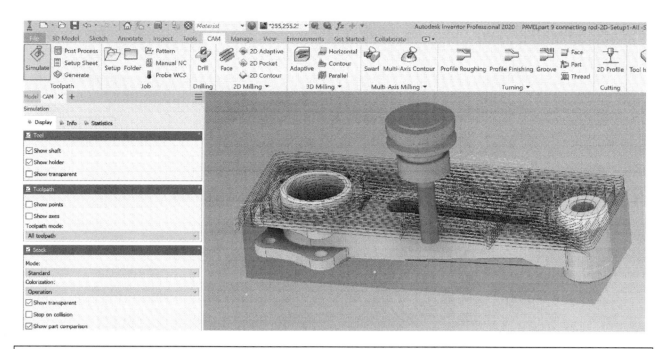

Post Processing

Now we are ready to create the CNC program. Select the operation click on the *Post Processor* on the top of the menu tab. Click on the pulldown menu and select FANUC/Fanuc (next to Open Confi button). In the *Program name or number* slot, change the program to 1020 or the desired number. Remember the numbers and where you saved your program. Click on *Post* to save the program to the desired Folder. This time we will create all machining processes in one program. Select the *Setup1* and run the on *Post Processor*, save to new program number 1020. The program will contain two operations, facing and contour, including all tool changes.

A new window *Autodesk Edit CAM (HSM) Edit* pops up with your new program inside. If the *Backlot* is selected, the postprocessor simulation window shows on the right.

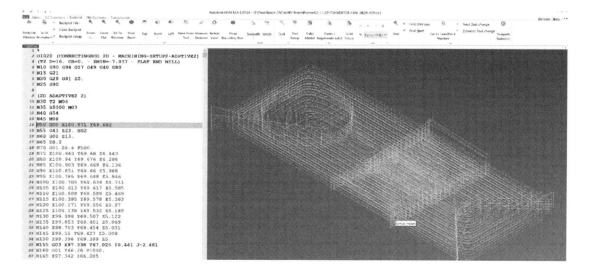

2D Slot

Now we will machine the second slot on *Setup2*. From the *CAM* menu select *2D* Milling pulldown menu and select *Slot*, a new sub-window appears with several tabs, the first one is the Tool. Click on the Tool button.

We need to select a tool from the library. On the left side, there are *All Tools* and *Sample library* with submenus. On the right side, select the same tool **#4-Ø5mm flat (5mm flat mill)** we used in one of the previous processes and finish by clicking *Select* on the bottom right. The tool is selected, and its number and size appear next to *Tool: #4-Ø5mm flat*.

Select *Geometry* next to the *Tool* tab, click on *Pocke selections,* and select the top outside of the slot; it will change the color to blue when selected. This machining operation will only machine the slot with the width equal to the tool size.

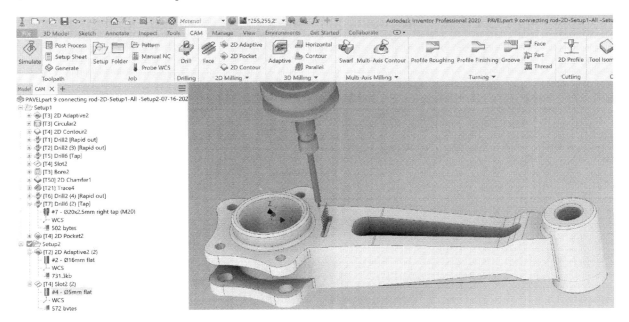

The rest of the tabs *Height*, *Passes*, and *Linking* menus will not be modified for this part of the operation. More detail for each tab will be given later with other operations.

Compete the operation by clicking *OK* on the bottom left side of the sub-window. Now the operation *[T4] Slot2 (2)* is created as part of the *Setup2*. It has submenus Tool number, WCS, and size of the program in bytes. Note that this process is machining from the top of the stock, with zigzag Z-axis steps, until the full depth is reached.

Simulation

We can simulate all the *2D Circular* process by selecting *Simulate* on the main tab. A new simulation window pops up, and the control buttons are the same as described above. You can select the checkbox *Stock* and then choose *Material: Show Transparent and Show Part comparison* to see stock and additional details. Click on the *Close* button and go back to the *CAM* menu. Save the Inventor file that now includes *[T4]Slot2 (2)* simulation.

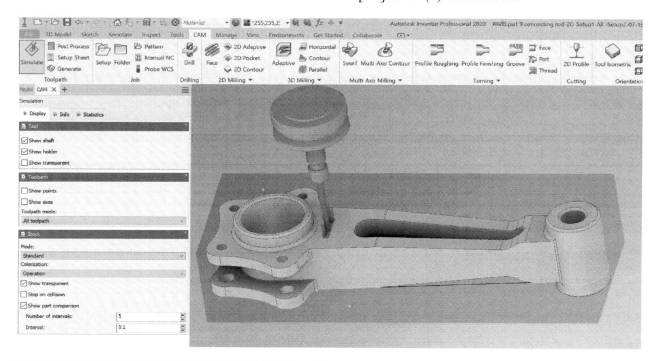

Post Processing

Now we are ready to create the next CNC program. Select the operation click on the *Post Processor* on the top of the menu tab. Click on the pulldown menu and Select FANUC/Fanuc (next to Open Confi button). In the *Program name or number* slot, change the program to 1021 or the desired number. Remember the numbers and where you saved your program. Click on *Post* to save the program to the desired Folder. This time we will create all machining processes in one program. Select the *Setup1* and run the on *Post Processor*, save to new program number 1021. The program will contain two operations, facing and contour, including all tool changes.

A new window *Autodesk Edit CAM (HSM) Edit* pops up with your new program inside. If the *Backlot* is selected, the postprocessor simulation window shows on the right.

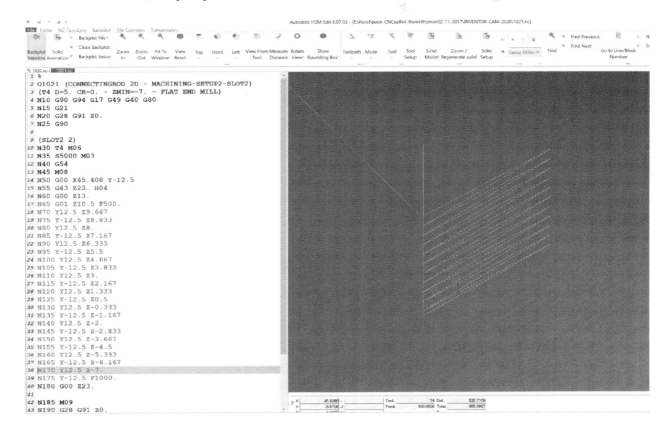

Notes:
_____

Notes:

Chapter 8

CNC Programming with Inventor CAM:

3D Machining

3D Machining using Inventor CAM

We describe 2D machining so far and now we move to 3D machining since some of the surfaces of this part can't be machined with 2D processes.

Setup 3

We will machine the neck between the bottom and top flanges, at different orientation using *Setup3*.

Click on *Setup*; we will use the same *Stock* from *Setup1*. Next, select the *Setup3* tab to change the position of the coordinate system.

Origin: select *Point* and click on a point on the part (e.g., top-left cylinder). The origin will move to that point, if the orientations of X, Y Z axis are not on the desired direction, use *Orientation:* to revert to the desired direction. Z-axis direction is alongside the part and pointing away from the part.

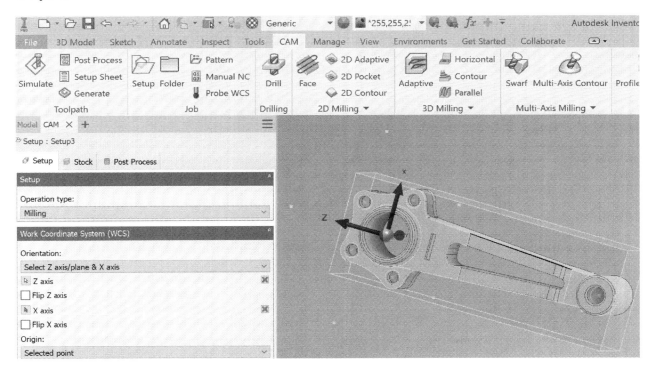

3D Adaptive

Select *Adaptive* from the *3D Milling* menu, a new *Adaptive: Adaptive3* sub-window appears with several tabs; the first is the Tool. Click on the Tool button.

We need to select a tool from the library. On the left side, there are *All Tools* and *Sample library* with submenus. On the right window, select the tool **#4-Ø5mm flat (5mm flat mill),** we used it in the previous operations, and finish the operation by clicking *Select* on the bottom right. The new tool is selected, and its number and size appear next to *Tool: #4-Ø5mm flat.*

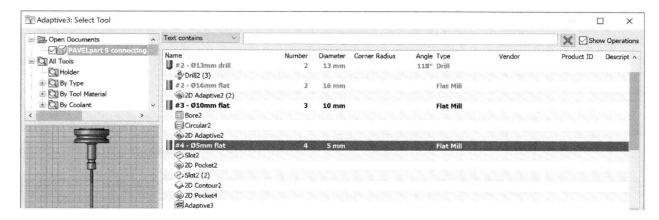

Select *Geometry* next to the *Tool* tab, and select the top part of the cylindrical surface between flanges; it will change the color to blue when selected. Next, select the checkbox of *Rest Machining* and below select *Rest material source: From previous operation(s).*

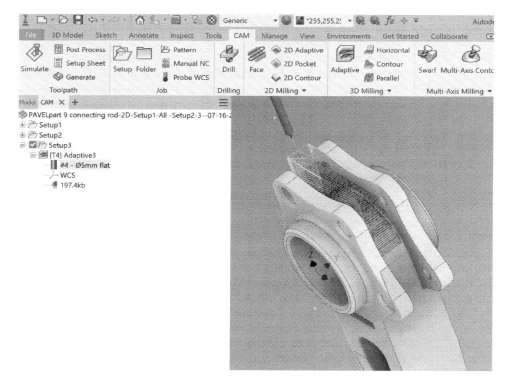

The rest of the tabs *Height*, *Passes*, and *Linking* menus will not be modified for this part of the operation. More detail for each tab will be given later with other operations.

Compete the operation by clicking *OK* on the bottom left side of the 2D Adaptive sub-window. Now the operation *[T4] Adaptive3* is created as part of the *Setup1*. It has submenus Tool number, WCS, and size of the program in bytes. Note that this process is machining at the steps hight define by the 3D adaptive process.

Simulation

We can simulate all the *3D Adaptive* process by selecting *Simulate* on the main tab. A new simulation window pops up, and the control buttons are the same as described above. You can select the checkbox *Stock* and then select *Material: Show Transparent and Show Part comparison* to see stock and additional details. Click on the *Close* button and go back to the *CAM* menu. Save the Inventor file that now includes *3D Adaptive* CAM simulation.

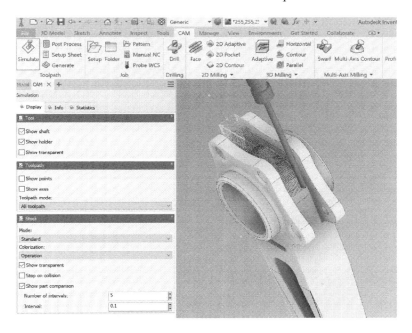

Note that the tool changes its color to red when there is a collision between the tool/holder with the part. We will increase the tool length to remove these collisions. Edit *[T4] Adaptive3* process, double-click on it, select tool, click on the *Tool: #4-Ø5mm flat*, select Edit, a new *Tool: #4-Ø5mm flat* windows with several taps on the tops pops-up. Select the *Cutter* tab and increase the lengths as follows: *Shoulder length: 75 mm, Flute length: 78 mm, Body length: 100 mm, Overall length 120 mm*. Click OK, a new small popup window appears: *Tool data changes cannot be made*. Select OK, then back on tool menu, click on *Select* to complete the tool modification. Note that tool size modifications apply for all operations that use this tool. The tool is not the standard, so if you use this program for machining, you need to make modifications for the tool you have. Now run the simulation again and see that no collision will occur.

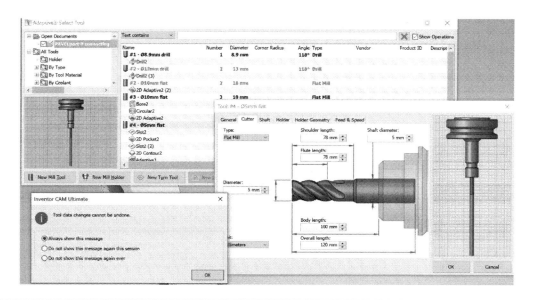

Now we are ready to create the third CNC program. Select the operation click on the *Post Processor* on the top of the menu tab. Click on the pulldown menu and Select FANUC/Fanuc (next to Open Confi button). In the *Program name or number* slot, change the program to 1021 or the desired number. Remember the numbers and where you saved your program. Click on *Post* to save the program to the desired Folder. This time we will create all machining processes in one program. Select the *Setup3* and run the on *Post Processor*, save to new program number 1021. The program will contain two operations, facing and contour, including all tool changes.

A new window *Autodesk Edit CAM (HSM) Edit* pops up with your new program inside. If the *Backlot* is selected, the postprocessor simulation window shows on the right.

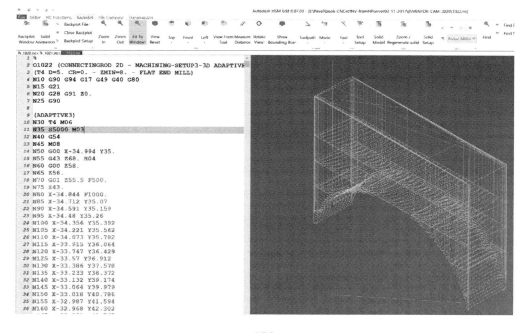

3D Adaptive Machining of inclined surface using Setup1

Next, we will machine the top inclined surface with a curvature. This surface was left after 2D machining of the part using *Setup1*.

We will copy the adaptive process from the Setup3 and will make some modifications. Under *Setup3,* select the operation *[T4] Adaptive3* and copy it, right-click *Copy*, or use *Ctr+C*. Go to *Setup1* and paste it right-click *Paste*, or use *Ctr+V*. *[T4] Adaptive3 (2)* appears as the last operation on *Setup1*.

Select *Geometry* next to the *Tool* tab, and select the top part of the inclined surfaces together with curvilinear surfaces; it will change the color to blue when selected. Next, select the checkbox of *Rest Machining* and below select *Rest material source: From previous operation(s)*.

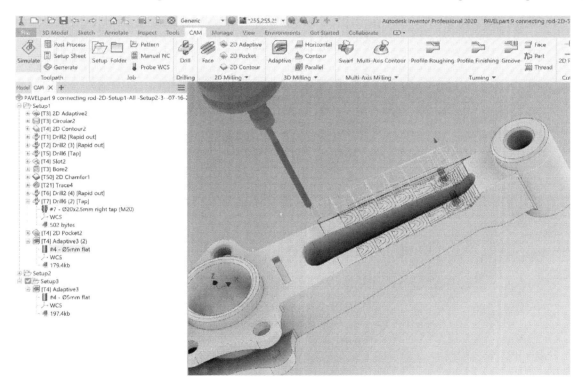

Notice that the machining result is not completed well on the curvilinear parts, and there are many rough steps to create the inclined slope. Since the toot *5mm flat* mill can't machine the wall, the inclined, and curvilinear surfaces at the bottom of the feature. To machine these surfaces, we will use a special ball-end tool. Double click on *[T4] Adaptive3 (2)* to edit it.

We need to select a new tool from the library. On the left side, there are *All Tools* and *Sample library* with submenus. Select Tutorial –Metric and on the right window select tool **#21-Ø6mm**

ball (6mm Ball Mill), and finish by clicking *Select* on the bottom right. The new tool is selected, and its number and size appear next to *Tool: #21-Ø6mm ball.*

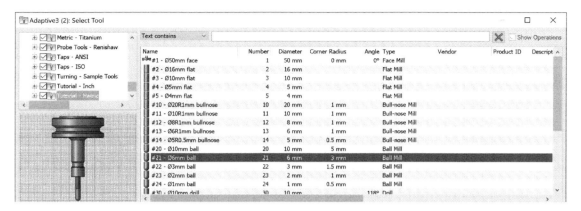

The rest of the tabs *Height*, *Passes*, and *Linking* menus will not be modified for this part of the operation. More detail for each tab will be given later with other operations.

Compete the operation by clicking *OK* on the bottom left side of the 2D Adaptive sub-window. Now the operation *[T21] Adaptive3(2)* is created as part of the *Setup1*. It has submenus Tool number, WCS, and size of the program in bytes. If you select *[T4] Adaptive3 (2),* the tool paths will show on the main window. Note that this process is machining at the steps hight define by the 3D adaptive process.

Simulation

We can simulate all the *3D Adaptive* processes by selecting *Simulate* on the main tab. A new simulation window pops up, and the control buttons are the same as described above. You can select the checkbox *Stock* and then select *Material: Show Transparent and Show Part comparison* to see stock and additional details. Click on the *Close* button and go back to the *CAM* menu. Save the Inventor file that now includes *3D Adaptive (2)* CAM simulation.

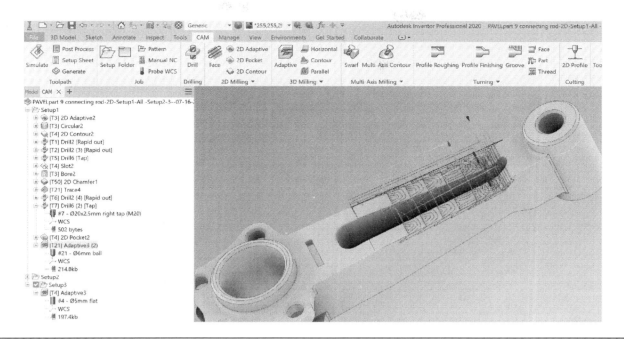

Post Processing

Now we are ready to create the CNC program. Select the operation click on the *Post Processor* on the top of the menu tab. Click on the pulldown menu and select FANUC/Fanuc (next to Open Confi button). In the *Program name or number* slot, change the program to 1023 or the desired number. Remember the numbers and where you saved your program. Click on *Post* to save the program to the desired Folder. This time we will create all machining processes in one program. Select the *Setup1* and run the on *Post Processor*, save to new program number 1023. The program will contain two operations, facing and contour, including all tool changes.

A new window *Autodesk Edit CAM (HSM) Edit* pops up with your new program inside. If the *Backlot* is selected, the postprocessor simulation window shows on the right.

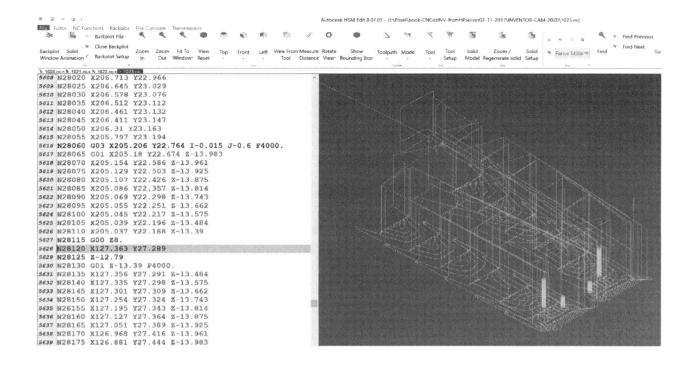

3D Adaptive of inclined surface using Setup2

Next, we will machine the bottom inclined surface with a curvature left after machining the part using *Setup2*. We will copy the adaptive process from the *Setup1* and will make some modifications

Under *Setup1,* select the operation *[T21] Adaptive3 (2)* and copy it, right-click *Copy*, or use *Ctr+C*. Go to *Setup2* and paste it right-click Paste, or use Ctr+V. [T21] Adaptive3 (3) appears as the last operation on Setup2.

Select *Geometry* next to the *Tool* tab, and select the top part of the inclined surface together with curvilinear surfaces; it will change the color to blue when selected. Next, select the checkbox of *Rest Machining* and below select *Rest material source: From previous operation(s).*

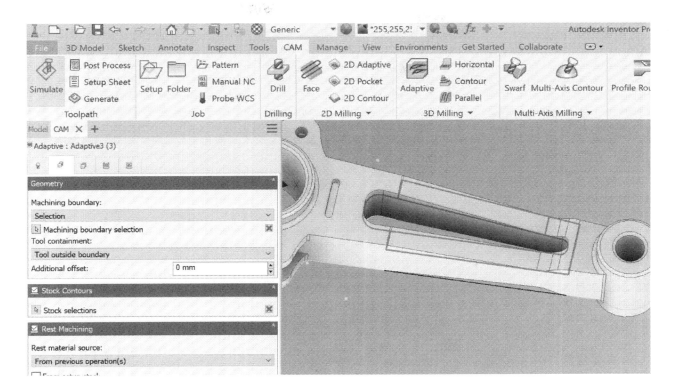

Simulation and Post Processing

We will not show more detail for this process since the inclined surface's geometry is symmetrical to the one on the other side. The CNC program File will be 1024. Therefore, the simulation and post-processing on Setup2 for *[T21] Adaptive3 (3)* look the same to one form Setup1, *[T21] Adaptive3 (2)*.

Advanced 2D/3D milling using tool orientation (1)

So far, we showed how to do machining using different setups and changing the coordinate systems accordingly. One of the advanced features of the Inventor CAM system programming is using the tool orientation with the same setup instead of making new. This process simplifies the CNC program preparation but should be used with caution. The tool is rotated to be perpendicular to the machined surface, which requires rotating the part position on the actual machine, manually or automatically rotating the tool table.

The last two surfaces that need to be machined are the flat surface between the flange and the sidewalls of the part.

We will use *Setup2* to create the machining, but any other setup can be used. Note that separate configuration setups for each wall can be the standard solution, depending on the actual application.

Select *Setup2,* then from the *2D Milling menu* select *2D Pocket.* Notice the default tool is set up perpendicular to the top surface. Change the tool to the one we used before, choos #3-Ø10mm *flat*

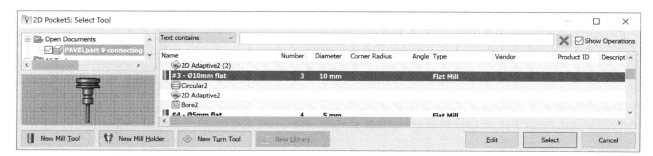

Select *Geometry* next to the *Tool* tab, and select the top part of the side surface; it will change the color to blue when selected. Next, select the checkbox of *Rest Machining* and below select *Rest material source: From previous operation(s).* Next, below click on *Tool Orientation*, leave the default *Tool orientation: Select Z axis/plane & X-axis,* click on the *Z-axis,* and then click again on the top part of the side surface. You will notice the change in the orientation (Z-axis pointing up from selected surface) of the coordinate system from *Setup1*.

176

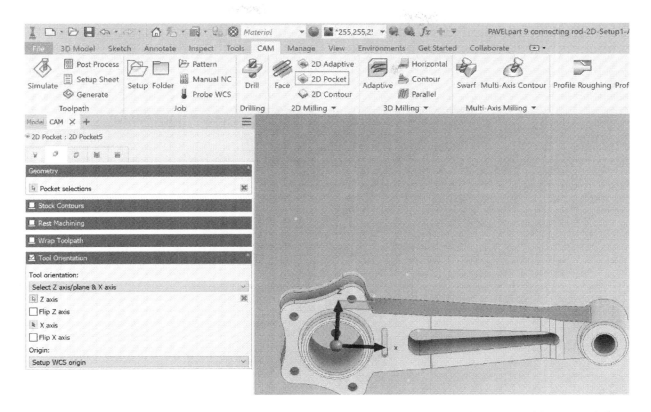

The rest of the tabs *Height*, *Passes*, and *Linking* menus will not be modified for this part of the operation. More detail for each tab will be given later with other operations.

Compete the operation by clicking *OK* on the bottom left side of the 2D Adaptive sub-window. Now the operation [*T3*] *Pocket5* is created as part of the *Setup2*. It has submenus Tool number, WCS, and size of the program in bytes. If you select [*T3*] *Pocket5,* the tool paths will show on the main window.

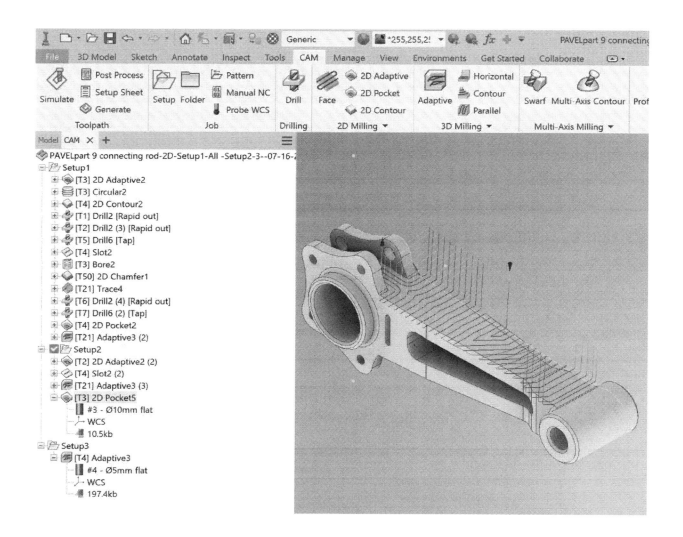

Simulation

We can simulate all the *[T3] Pocket5* process by selecting *Simulate* on the main tab. A new simulation window pops up, and the control buttons are the same as described above. You can select checkbox *Stock* and then select *Material: Show Transparent and Show Part comparison* to see stock and additional details. Click on the *Close* button and go back to the *CAM* menu.

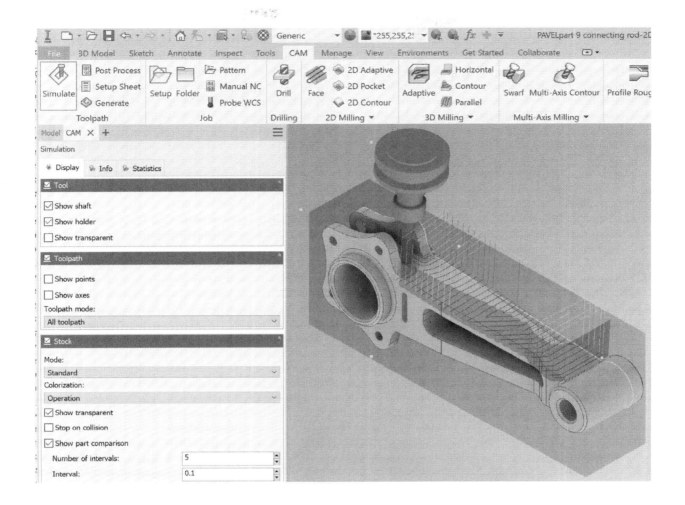

Post Processing

Now we are ready to create the CNC program. Select the operation click on the *Post Processor* on the top of the menu tab. Click on the pulldown menu and Select FANUC/Fanuc (next to Open Confi button). In the *Program name or number* slot, change the program to 1025 or the desired number. Select the process *[T3] Pocket5* under *Setup1* and run the on *Post Processor*, save to new program number 1025.

A new window *Autodesk Edit CAM (HSM) Edit* pops up with your new program inside. If the *Backlot* is selected, the postprocessor simulation window shows on the right.

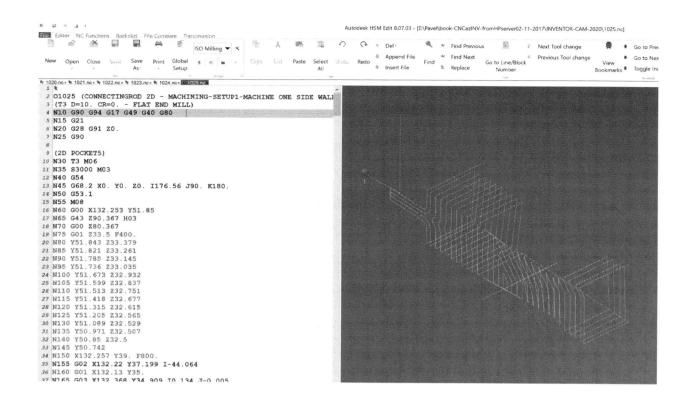

```
 1  %
 2  O1025 (CONNECTINGROD 2D - MACHINING-SETUP1-MACHINE ONE SIDE WALL
 3  (T3 D=10. CR=0. - FLAT END MILL)
 4  N10 G90 G94 G17 G49 G40 G80
 5  N15 G21
 6  N20 G28 G91 Z0.
 7  N25 G90
 8
 9  (2D POCKET5)
10  N30 T3 M06
11  N35 S3000 M03
12  N40 G54
13  N45 G68.2 X0. Y0. Z0. I176.56 J90. K180.
14  N50 G53.1
15  N55 M08
16  N60 G00 X132.253 Y51.85
17  N65 G43 Z90.367 H03
18  N70 G00 Z80.367
19  N75 G01 Z33.5 F400.
20  N80 Y51.843 Z33.379
21  N85 Y51.821 Z33.261
22  N90 Y51.785 Z33.145
23  N95 Y51.736 Z33.035
24  N100 Y51.673 Z32.932
25  N105 Y51.599 Z32.837
26  N110 Y51.513 Z32.751
27  N115 Y51.418 Z32.677
28  N120 Y51.315 Z32.615
29  N125 Y51.205 Z32.565
30  N130 Y51.089 Z32.529
31  N135 Y50.971 Z32.507
32  N140 Y50.85 Z32.5
33  N145 Y50.742
34  N150 X132.257 Y39. F800.
35  N155 G02 X132.22 Y37.199 I-44.064
36  N160 G01 X132.13 Y35.
37  N165 G03 X132.368 Y34.909 I0.134 J-0.005
```

Advanced 2D/3D milling using tool orientation (2)

Creating the program for the opposite sidewall is identical to the one show before, we can use duplicate on the same *Setup1* or again use copy and paste to *Setup2*. Next in the Geometry, select the new pocket, then select the new tool orientation that flips the coordinate system.

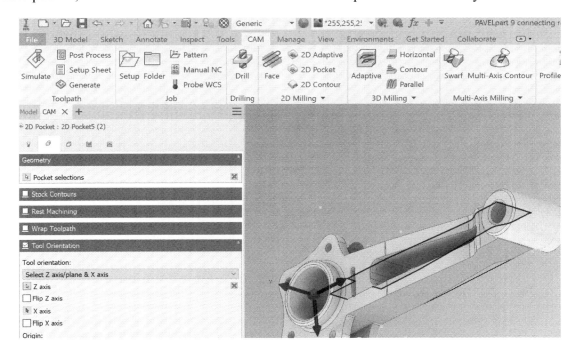

The operation will look similar to the first sidewall.

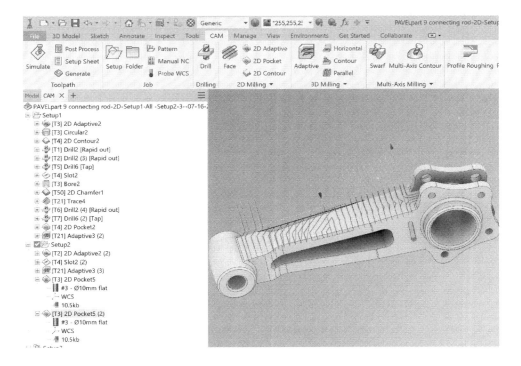

The simulation will look the same as the first sidewall.

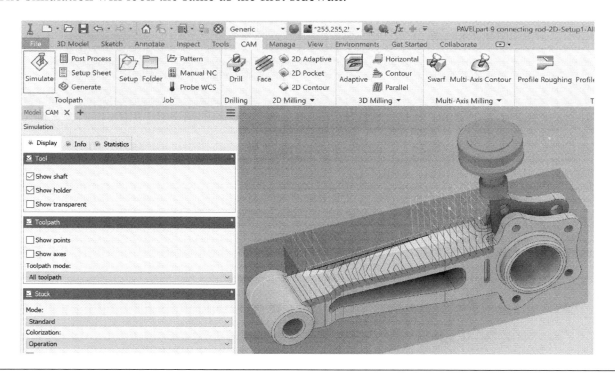

Post processing will also look similar to the first sidewall; only the CNC program number will be changed to 2026.

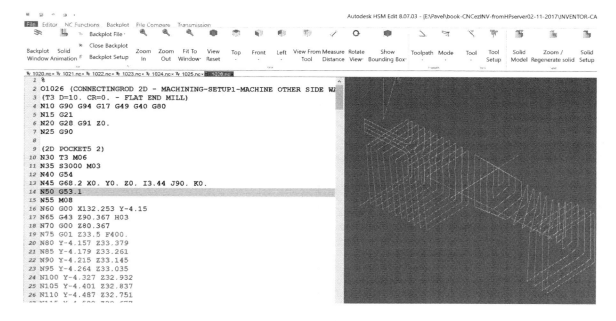

Inventor 3D CAM machining - Advanced 3D milling

3D Milling

There are several most common *2D Milling* operations in Inventor CAM, shown on the ribbon menu: *Adaptive, Horizontal, Contour, Parallel*. Additional operations are available by selecting *3D Milling* pulldown menu: *Pocket, Scallop, Pencil, Radial, Spiral, Morphed Spiral, Ramp, Project, Morph, Flow*. Also, *Multi-Axis Milling* has *Swarf and Multi-Axis Control*. The last options required CNC machine with 4 or 5 axis control. We will try to explain and show machining with these 3D Milling processes.

Setup settings for the stock and coordinate system were explained in previous chapters. Since the process is the same, we will not explain the details at this time.

3D Adaptive

3D Adaptive is a rough milling process to clear a lot of the material working in the Z-axis direction. Select *Adaptive* from *CAM* menu, a new Adaptive: sub-window appears with several tabs, the first is the *Tool*. We need to select a tool from the library. On the left side, there are *All Tools* and *Sample library* with submenus. Select *Sample Library →Tutorial-metric (or other)*, then on the right window select tool **#3-Ø10mm flat (Flat Mill)** and finish by clicking *Select* on the bottom right. The A new tool is selected, and its number and size appear next to *Tool*: #3-Ø10mm flat (Flat Mill).

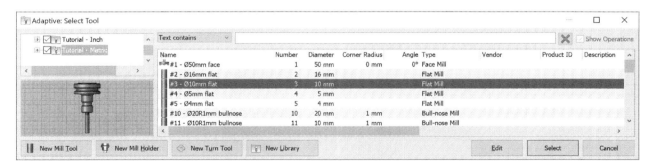

Next, on the *Geometry* tap, select *Stock selections* and click on the top of the part, leave the rest of the parameters unchecked.

Next to the *Geometry* tab are *Height, Passes*, and *Linking* menus, which will not be altered for this operation. We will explain more detail for each tab when we use them with other operations later.

Complete this operation by clicking on *OK* on the bottom of the right sub-window. Now the A new operation *[T3] Adaptive* is created under the *Setup1*. It has submenus Tool number, WCS, and size of the program in bytes. If you select on the *[T3] Adaptive,* the tool path profile (blue/green lines) will show on the main window.

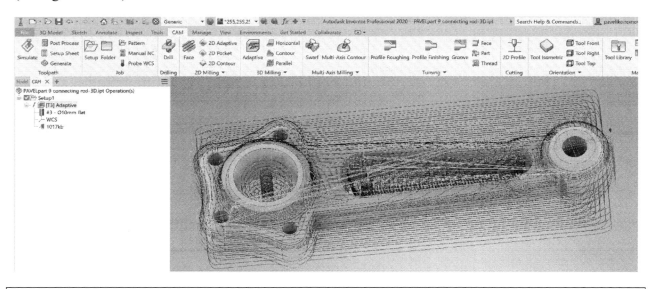

Simulation

We can simulate all the *3D Adaptive* process by selecting *Simulate* on the main tab. A new simulation window pops up, and the control buttons are the same as described above. You can select the checkbox *Stock* and then select *Material: Show Transparent* and *Show Part comparison* to see stock and additional details. *Click* on the *Close* button and go back to the *CAM* menu. Save the Inventor file that now includes *3D Adaptive* CAM simulation.

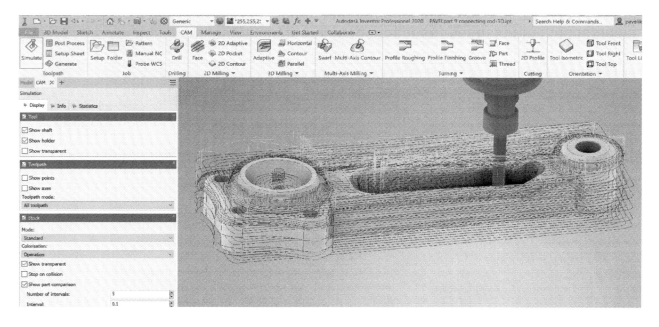

Now we are ready to create the CNC program. Select the operation, click on the *Post Processor* on the top of the menu tab. Click on the pulldown menu and Select FANUC/Fanuc (next to Open Config button). In the *Program name or number* slot, change the program to 1030 or desired number. Remember the numbers and where you saved your program. Click on *Post* to save the program to the desired folder.

A new window *Autodesk Edit CAM (HSM) Edit* pops up with the new program inside.

3D Horizontal

3D *Horizontal* clearing is a special facing milling process that detects flat planes and machines them in an offsetting path on the Z-axis direction. It is used in finishing or semi-finishing operations.

Select *Horizontal* from *CAM* menu, a new *Horizontal*: sub-window appears with several tabs, the first is the *Tool*. We need to select a tool from the library. On the left side, there are *All Tools* and *Sample library* with submenus. Select *Sample Library→Tutorial-metric (or other)*, then on the right window select tool **#8-Ø8mm flat (Flat Mill)** and finish by clicking *Select* on the bottom right. The new tool is selected, and its number and size appear next to *Tool: #8-Ø8mm flat (Flat Mill)*.

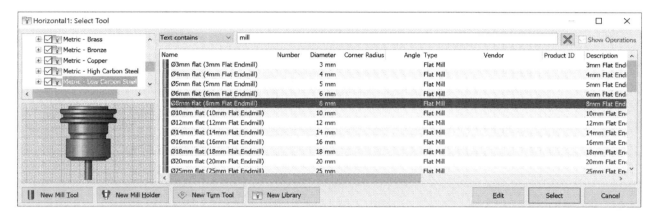

Next to the *Tool* tab are *Geometry, Height, Passes*, and *Linking* menus, which will not be altered for this operation. We will explain more detail for each menu tab when we use them with other operations later.

Complete this operation by clicking on *OK* on the bottom of the right sub-window. Now the new operation *[T8] Horizontal* is created under the *Setup1*. It has submenus Tool number, WCS, and size of the program in bytes. If you select the *[T8] Horizontal,* the tool path profile (blue/green lines) will show on the main window.

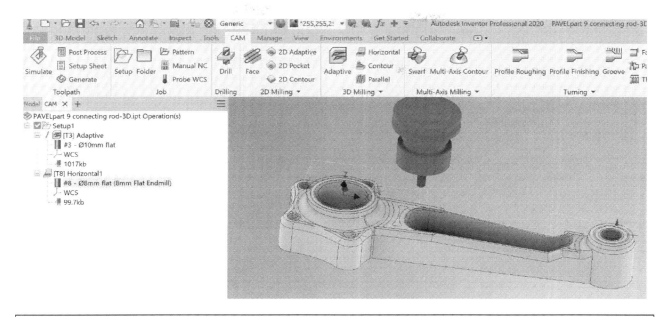

Simulation

We can simulate all the *3D Horizontal* process by selecting *Simulate* on the main tab. A new simulation window pops up, and the control buttons are the same as described above. You can select the checkbox *Stock* and then choose *Material: Show Transparent and Show Part comparison* to see stock and additional details. *Click* on the *Close* button and go back to the *CAM* menu. Save the Inventor file.

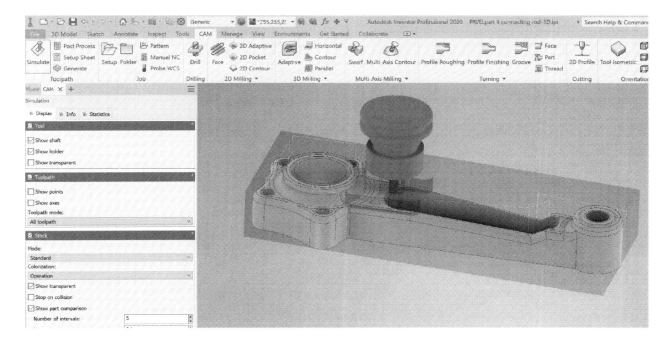

Now we are ready to create the next CNC program. Select the operation, click on the *Post Processor* on the top of the menu tab. Click on the pulldown menu and Select FANUC/Fanuc (next to Open Config button). In the *Program name or number* slot, change the program to 1031 or the desired number. Remember the numbers and where you saved your program.

A new window *Autodesk Edit CAM (HSM) Edit* pops up with your A new program inside. If the *Backplot* is selected, the postprocessor simulation window shows on the right.

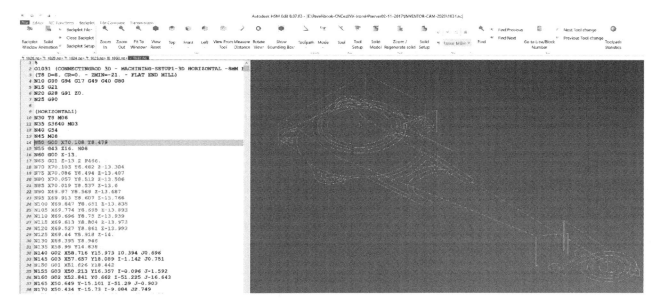

3D Contour

The *Contour* in *3D Milling* is used in finishing or semi-finishing operations for clearing vertical or steep walls milling. *Contour* (also called waterline) keep constant step down. You can specify the slope angle (30-90) for steep walls.

Select *Contour* from *CAM* menu, a new *Contour*: sub-window appears with several tabs, the first is the *Tool*. We need to select a tool from the library. In the right window, select the tool **#8-Ø8mm flat (Flat Mill)**, the same one we used in the previous operation, and finish by clicking *Select* on the bottom right. The A new tool is selected, and its number and size appear next to *Tool: #8-Ø8mm flat (8 mm Flat End Mill)*.

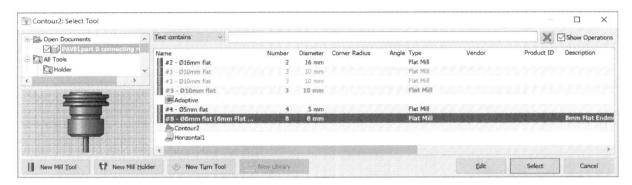

On Geometry tab, select the big slot, below make changes, select the checkbox of the *Slope:,* and modify the parameters beneath *From slope angle: 80 deg* and *To Slope Angle: 90 deg*. Next to the *Tool* tab are *Height, Passes*, and *Linking* menus, which will not be altered for this operation.

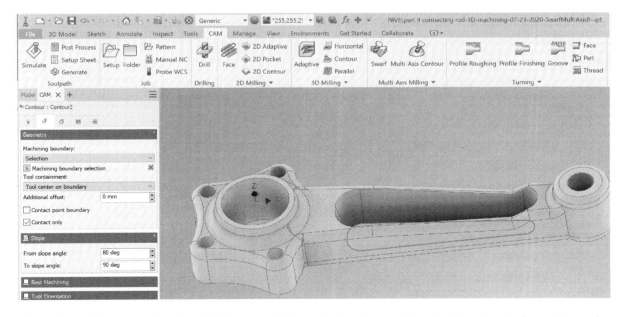

Complete this operation by clicking on *OK* on the bottom of the right sub-window. Now the new operation *[T8] Contour2* is created under the *Setup1*. It has submenus Tool number, WCS, and size of the program in bytes. If you select on the *[T8] Contour2,* the tool path profile (blue/green) lines) will show on the main window.

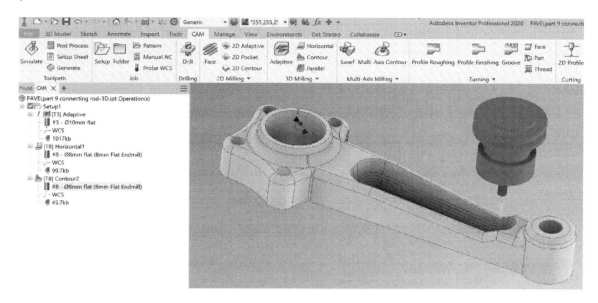

Simulation

We can simulate all the *3D Contour* process by selecting *Simulate* on the main tab. A new simulation window pops up, and the control buttons are the same as described above. You can select the checkbox *Stock* and then choose *Material: Show Transparent and Show Part comparison* to see stock and additional details. If you run the simulation, it is clear that there is a collision of the tool or holder with the part. Modify the tool length (explained earlier) and rerun the simulation to verify that there is no collision. Click on the *Close* button and go back to the *CAM* menu. Save the Inventor file.

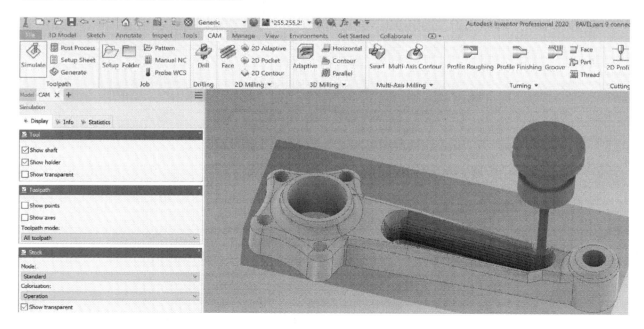

Now we are ready to create the CNC program. Select the operation click on the *Post Processor* on the top of the menu tab. Click on the pulldown menu and Select FANUC/Fanuc (next to Open Config button). In the *Program name or number* slot, change the program to 1032 or the desired number. Remember the numbers and where you saved your program.

A new window *Autodesk Edit CAM (HSM) Edit* pops up with your A new program inside. If the *Backplot* is selected, the postprocessor simulation window shows on the right.

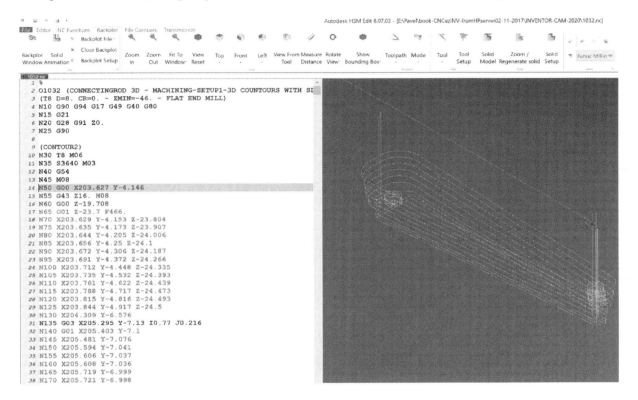

3D Parallel

Parallel in *3D Milling* is used in finishing operations with surfaces parallel to X, Y plane, and following Z directions. We will use this process for machining the rounded filets and inclined surfaces of the part.

Select *Parallel* from *CAM* menu, a new *Parallel*: sub-window appears with several tabs, the first is the *Tool*. Since the operation is for 3D machining, we will select a new ball-end tool. Select *Sample Library* →*Tutorial-metric (or other)*, then on the right window select tool **#20-Ø10mm ball (Ball Mill)** and finish by clicking *Select* on the bottom right. The new tool is selected, and its number and size appear next to *Tool: #20-Ø10mm ball (Ball Mill)*.

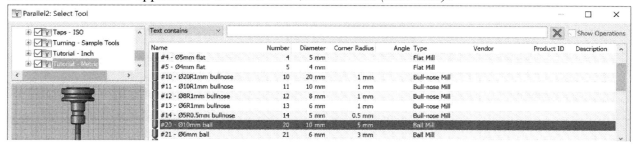

On the Geometry tab, select the top surface, then make changes, in the *Rest material source: From previous operation(s)*. Next in the *Passes* tab, change the *Setove: 2 mm. Height* and *Linking* menus will not be altered for this operation.

Complete this operation by clicking on *OK* on the bottom of the right sub-window. Now the A new operation *[T20] Parallel* is created under the *Setup1*. It has submenus Tool number, WCS, and size of the program in bytes. If you select the tool *#20-Ø10 mm ball*, the tool path profile (blue/green lines) will show on the main window.

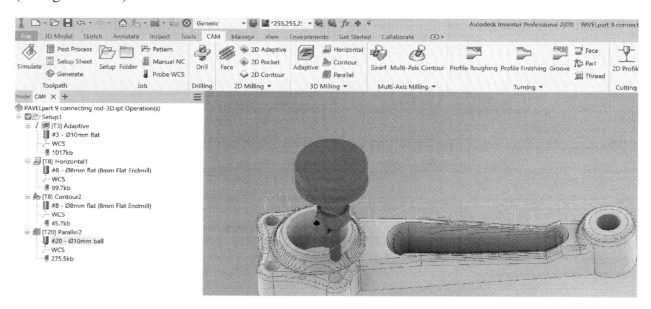

We can simulate all the *3D Parallel* process by selecting *Simulate* on the main tab. A new simulation window pops up, and the control buttons are the same as described above. You can select the checkbox *Stock* and then chooose *Material: Show Transparent and Show Part comparison* to see stock and additional details. *Click* on the *Close* button and go back to the *CAM* menu. Save the Inventor file.

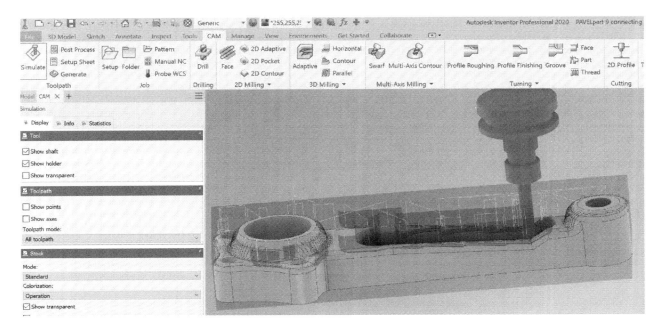

Post Processing

Now we are ready to create the CNC program. Select the operation click on the *Post Processor* on the top of the menu tab. Click on the pulldown menu and Select FANUC/Fanuc (next to Open Config button). In the *Program name or number* slot, change the program to 1033 or the desired number. Remember the numbers and where you saved your program.

A new window *Autodesk Edit CAM (HSM) Edit* pops up with your A new program inside. If the *Backplot* is selected, the postprocessor simulation window shows on the right.

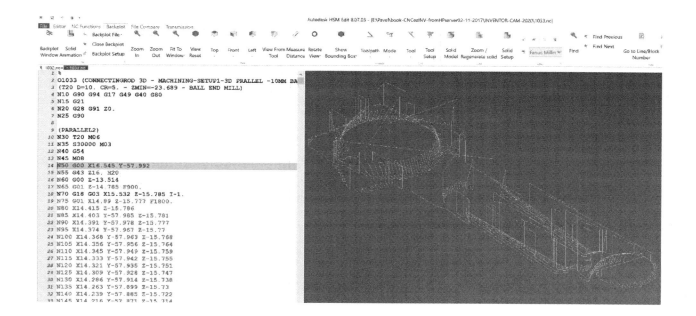

```
1  %
2  O1033 (CONNECTINGROD 3D - MACHINING-SETUP1-3D PRALLEL -10MM BA
3  (T20 D=10. CR=5. - ZMIN=-23.689 - BALL END MILL)
4  N10 G90 G94 G17 G49 G40 G80
5  N15 G21
6  N20 G28 G91 Z0.
7  N25 G90
8
9  (PARALLEL2)
10 N30 T20 M06
11 N35 S30000 M03
12 N40 G54
13 N45 M08
14 N50 G00 X16.545 Y-57.992
15 N55 G43 Z16. H20
16 N60 G00 Z-13.514
17 N65 G01 Z-14.785 F900.
18 N70 G18 G03 X15.532 Z-15.785 I-1.
19 N75 G01 X14.89 Z-15.777 F1800.
20 N80 X14.415 Z-15.786
21 N85 X14.403 Y-57.985 Z-15.781
22 N90 X14.391 Y-57.978 Z-15.777
23 N95 X14.374 Y-57.967 Z-15.77
24 N100 X14.368 Y-57.963 Z-15.768
25 N105 X14.356 Y-57.956 Z-15.764
26 N110 X14.345 Y-57.949 Z-15.759
27 N115 X14.333 Y-57.942 Z-15.755
28 N120 X14.321 Y-57.935 Z-15.751
29 N125 X14.309 Y-57.928 Z-15.747
30 N130 X14.286 Y-57.914 Z-15.738
31 N135 X14.263 Y-57.899 Z-15.73
32 N140 X14.239 Y-57.885 Z-15.722
33 N145 X14.216 Y-57.871 Z-15.714
```

194

3D Pocket

In 3D Milling, Pocket is a rough milling process to clear a lot of material layer by layer. From the pulldown menu of the *3D Milling,* choose *Pocket*, a new *Pocket*: sub-window appears with several tabs, the first one is the *Tool*. We need to select a tool from the library. In the right window, select the tool **#8-Ø8mm flat (Flat Mill)**, the same one we used in the previous operation, and finish by clicking *Select* on the bottom right. The A new tool is selected, and its number and size appear next to *Tool: #8-Ø8mm flat (8 mm Flat Endmill).*

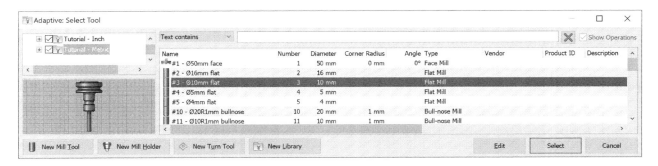

Next on the *Geometry* tap select *Stock Contours* and click on the part, leave the rest of the parameters unchecked.

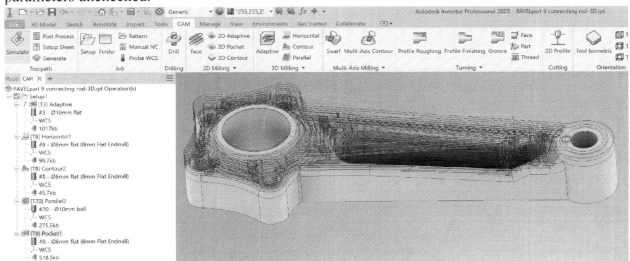

Double click on *[T8] Pocket1* to edit it. Next to the *Geometry* tab, select *Passes* and modify *Maxim roughing stepdown: 2mm*. Then select tab *Linking* and modify the *Ramp type:* to *Plunge outside stock*. This chabges will reduce the helix paths (red circles) and overall program length. The tabs *Height* will not be altered for this operation.

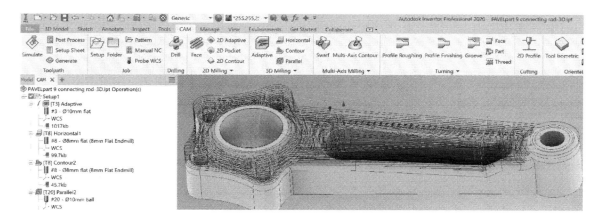

Complete this operation by clicking on *OK* on the bottom of the right sub-window. Now the A new operation *[T8] Pocket1* is created under the *Setup1*. It has submenus Tool number, WCS, and size of the program in bytes. If you select on the *#8-Ø8mm flat (8 mm Flat Endmill),* the tool path profile (blue/green lines) will show on the main window.

Simulation

We can simulate all the *3D Pocket1* process by selecting *Simulate* on the main tab. A new simulation window pops up, and the control buttons are the same as described above. You can select the checkbox *Stock* and then select *Material: Show Transparent and Show Part comparison* to see stock and additional details. *Click* on the *Close* button and go back to the *CAM* menu. Save the Inventor file that now includes *3D Adaptive* CAM simulation.

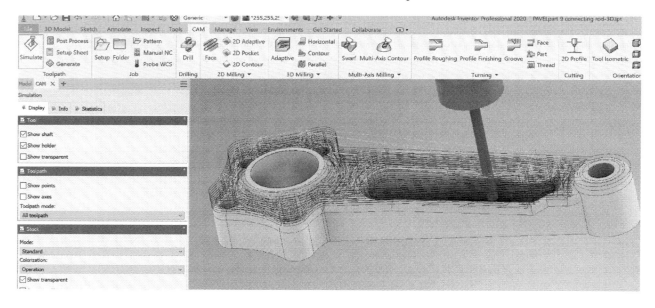

Now we are ready to create the CNC program. Select the operation click on the *Post Processor* on the top of the menu tab. Click on the pulldown menu and Select FANUC/Fanuc (next to Open Config button). In the *Program name or number* slot, change the program to 1034 or the desired number. Remember the numbers and where you saved your program.

A new window *Autodesk Edit CAM (HSM) Edit* pops up with your A new program inside. If the *Backplot* is selected, the postprocessor simulation window shows on the right.

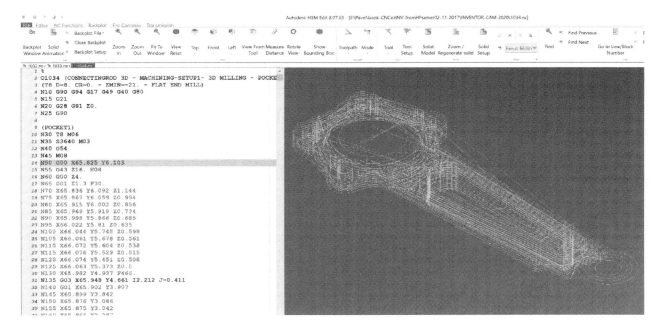

3D Scallop

In *3D Milling, Scallop* is finishing milling operations using passes constant offset passes. From the pulldown menu, select *Scallop*; a new *Scallop*: sub-window appears with several tabs, the first is the *Tool*. Since the operation is for 3D machining we will select A new ball-end tool. Select *Sample Library→Metric-Low Carbon Steel* *(or other for different material)*, then on the right window select tool **Ø8mm ball (Ball Mill)** and finish by clicking *Select* on the bottom right. The new tool is selected, and its number and size appear next to *Tool: #1-Ø8mm ball (Ball Endmill)*.

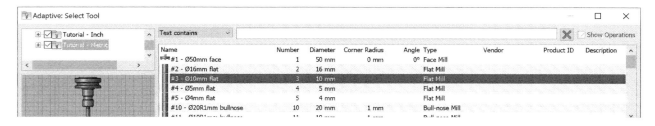

Next on the *Geometry* tap select *Machining boundary: Selection* and click on the outside edges of the big hole, leave the rest of the parameters unchecked. Next to the *Geometry* tab, select *Passes* and modify *Maxim roughing stepdown: 2mm*. The tabs *Height* and *Linking* will not be altered for this operation.

Complete this operation by clicking on *OK* on the bottom of the right sub-window. Now the A new operation *[T1] Scallop1* is created under the *Setup1*. It has submenus Tool number, WCS, and size of the program in bytes. If you select on the *#1-Ø8mm ball (Ball Endmill)*, the tool path profile (blue/green lines) will show on the main window.

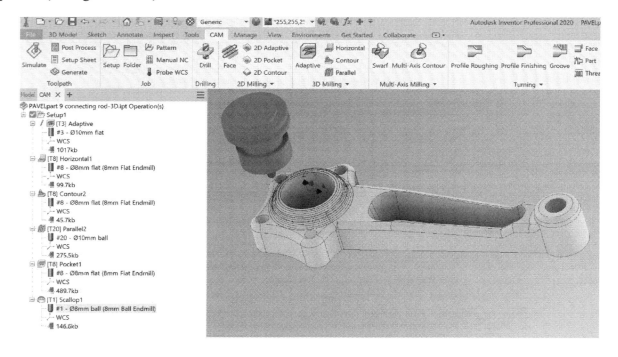

We can simulate all the *Scallop1* process by selecting *Simulate* on the main tab. A new simulation window pops up, and the control buttons are the same as described above. You can select the checkbox *Stock* and then select *Material: Show Transparent and Show Part comparison* to see stock and additional details. *Click* on the *Close* button and go back to the *CAM* menu. Save the Inventor file that now includes *3D* machining *Scallop1* CAM simulation.

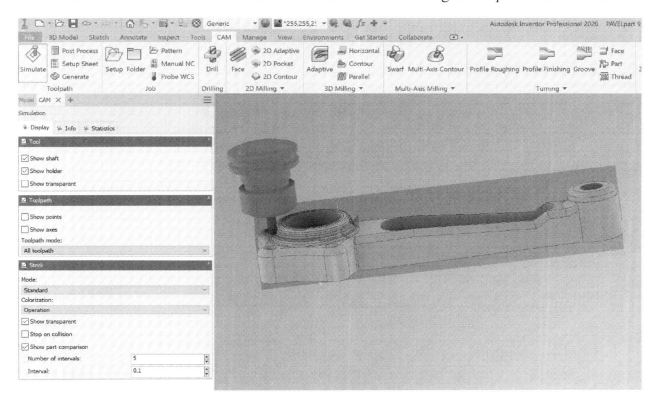

Post Processing

Now we are ready to create the CNC program. Select the operation click on the *Post Processor* on the top of the menu tab. Click on the pulldown menu and Select FANUC/Fanuc (next to Open Config button). In the *Program name or number* slot, change the program to 1035 or the desired number. Remember the numbers and where you saved your program.

A new window *Autodesk Edit CAM (HSM) Edit* pops up with your A new program inside. If the *Backplot* is selected, the postprocessor simulation window shows on the right.

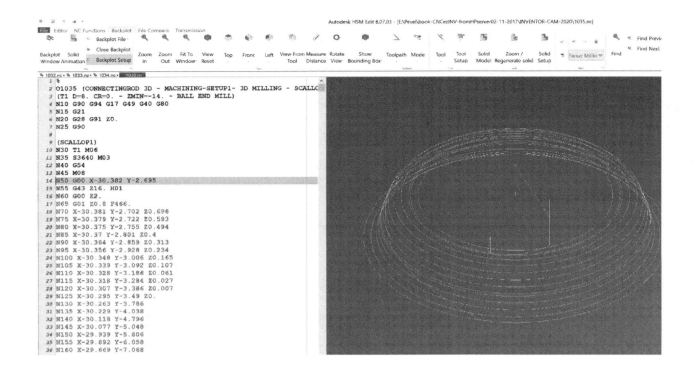

```
1  %
2  O1035 (CONNECTINGROD 3D - MACHINING-SETUP1- 3D MILLING - SCALLO
3  (T1 D=8. CR=0. - ZMIN=-14. - BALL END MILL)
4  N10 G90 G94 G17 G49 G40 G80
5  N15 G21
6  N20 G28 G91 Z0.
7  N25 G90
8
9  (SCALLOP1)
10 N30 T1 M06
11 N35 S3640 M03
12 N40 G54
13 N45 M08
14 N50 G00 X-30.382 Y-2.695
15 N55 G43 Z16. H01
16 N60 G00 Z2.
17 N65 G01 Z0.8 F466.
18 N70 X-30.381 Y-2.702 Z0.696
19 N75 X-30.379 Y-2.722 Z0.593
20 N80 X-30.375 Y-2.755 Z0.494
21 N85 X-30.37 Y-2.801 Z0.4
22 N90 X-30.364 Y-2.859 Z0.313
23 N95 X-30.356 Y-2.928 Z0.234
24 N100 X-30.348 Y-3.006 Z0.165
25 N105 X-30.339 Y-3.092 Z0.107
26 N110 X-30.328 Y-3.186 Z0.061
27 N115 X-30.318 Y-3.284 Z0.027
28 N120 X-30.307 Y-3.386 Z0.007
29 N125 X-30.295 Y-3.49 Z0.
30 N130 X-30.263 Y-3.786
31 N135 X-30.229 Y-4.038
32 N140 X-30.118 Y-4.796
33 N145 X-30.077 Y-5.048
34 N150 X-29.939 Y-5.806
35 N155 X-29.892 Y-6.058
36 N160 X-29.669 Y-7.068
```

3D Pencil

In *3D Milling, Pencil* is used after other finishing milling processes for filets and corners with relatively small radii. From the pulldown menu select *Pencil*, a new *Pencil:* sub-window appears with several tabs; the first is the *Tool*. Since the operation is for 3D machining, we will select a new ball-end tool. Select *Sample Library →Metric-Low Carbon Steel (or other for different material)*, then on the right window select tool **Ø5mm ball (Ball Mill)** and finish by clicking *Select* on the bottom right. The new tool is selected, and its number and size appear next to *Tool: #5-Ø5mm ball (Ball Endmill)*.

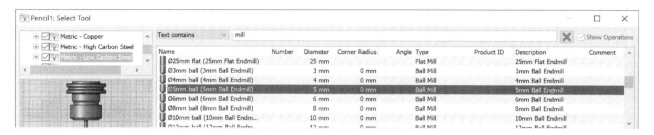

Next on the *Geometry* tap select *Machining boundary: Silhouette*, leave the rest of the parameters unchecked. The tabs *Height, Passes,* and *Linking* will not be altered for this operation.

Complete this operation by clicking on *OK* on the bottom of the right sub-window. Now the A new operation *[T5] Pencil1* is created under the *Setup1*. It has submenus Tool number, WCS, and size of the program in bytes. If you select on the *#5-Ø5mm ball (Ball Endmill),* the tool path profile (blue/green lines) will show on the main window.

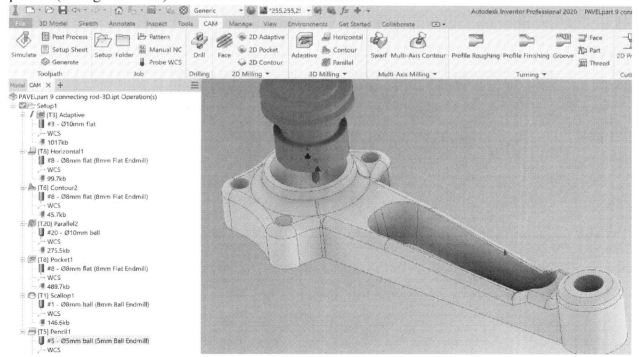

We can simulate the *3D Pencil1* process by selecting *Simulate* on the main tab. A new simulation window pops up, and the control buttons are the same as described above. If you run the simulation, it is clear that there is a collision of the tool or holder with the part. Modify the tool length (explained earlier) and run the simulation again to verify that there is no colision. You can select the checkbox *Stock* and then choose *Material: Show Transparent and Show Part comparison* to see stock and additional details. *Click* on the *Close* button and go back to the *CAM* menu. Save the Inventor file that now includes *3D* machining *Pencil1* CAM simulation.

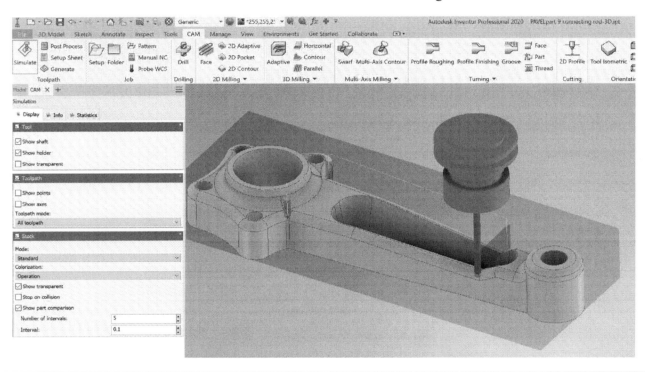

Now we are ready to create the CNC program. Select the operation click on the *Post Processor* on the top of the menu tab. Click on the pulldown menu and Select FANUC/Fanuc (next to Open Config button). In the *Program name or number* slot, change the program to 1036 or the desired number. Remember the numbers and where you saved your program.

A new window *Autodesk Edit CAM (HSM) Edit* pops up with your A new program inside. If the *Backplot* is selected, the postprocessor simulation window shows on the right.

File Editor NC Functions Backplot File Compare Transmission

Backplot Window Animation | Solid | Backplot File · | Close Backplot | Backplot Setup | Zoom In | Zoom Out | Fit To Window | View Reset | Top | Front | Left | View From Tool | Measure Distance | Rotate View | Show Bounding Box | Toolpath | Mode | Tool | Tool Setup | Solid Model | Zoom / Regenerate solid | Solid Setup | Fanuc Miller | Find

```
1  %
2  O1036 (CONNECTINGROD 3D - MACHINING-SETUP1- 3D MILLING - PENCIL
3  (T5 D=5. CR=2.5 - ZMIN=-24.113 - BALL END MILL)
4  N10 G90 G94 G17 G49 G40 G80
5  N15 G21
6  N20 G28 G91 Z0.
7  N25 G90
8
9  (PENCIL1)
10 N30 T5 M06
11 N35 S5820 M03
12 N40 G54
13 N45 M08
14 N50 G00 X34.962 Y-30.324
15 N55 G43 Z16. H05
16 N60 G00 Z-13.79
17 N65 G01 Z-16.128 F466.
18 N70 X34.964 Y-30.33 Z-16.213
19 N75 X34.972 Y-30.35 Z-16.295
20 N80 X34.985 Y-30.383 Z-16.372
21 N85 X35.002 Y-30.427 Z-16.442
22 N90 X35.023 Y-30.481 Z-16.503
23 N95 X35.094 Y-30.662 Z-16.674
24 N100 X35.128 Y-30.739 Z-16.751
25 N105 X35.156 Y-30.804 Z-16.805
26 N110 X35.188 Y-30.876 Z-16.846
27 N115 X35.222 Y-30.954 Z-16.872
28 N120 X35.257 Y-31.035 Z-16.882
29 N125 X35.293 Y-31.116 Z-16.877
30 N130 X35.327 Y-31.195 Z-16.856
```

3D Radial

In *3D Milling, Radial* is used for finishing milling processes, starting from a center point and moves in diagonal directions. From the pulldown menu select *Radial*, a new *Radial1*: sub-window appears with several tabs, the first is the *Tool*. We need to select a tool from the library. In the right window, select the tool **#5-Ø5mm ball (Ball Mill)**, the same one we used in the previous operation, and finish by clicking *Select* on the bottom right. The new tool is selected, and its number and size appear next to *Tool: #5-Ø5mm ball (5 mm Ball Endmill).*

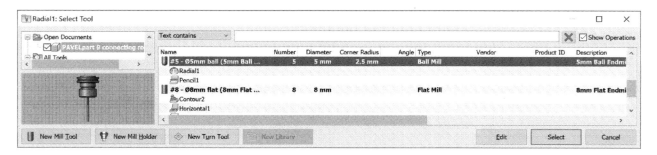

Next on the *Geometry* tap select Machining boundary: Silhouette, and click on the lower edge of the round fillet of the smaller cylinder. To machine rounded edges on the left to the cylinder, select and modify *Additional offset: 2mm.* On the *Height* tab, modify *Top offset -4 mm* to avoid machining of the round fillet on the top. The rest of the tabs *Passes* and *Linking* will not be altered for this operation.

Complete this operation by clicking on *OK* on the bottom of the right sub-window. Now the A new operation *[T5] Radial1* is created under the *Setup1*. It has submenus Tool number, WCS, and size of the program in bytes. If you select on the *#5-Ø5mm ball (Ball Endmill),* the tool path profile (blue/green lines) will show on the main window.

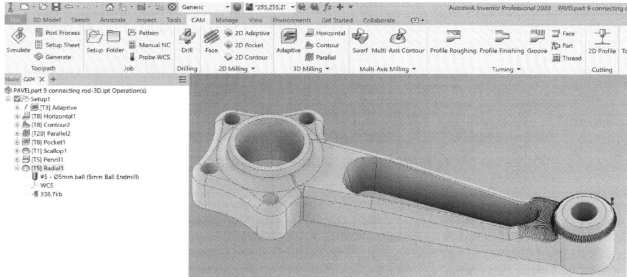

We can simulate all the *3D Radial1* process by selecting *Simulate* on the main tab. A new simulation window pops up, and the control buttons are the same as described above. You can select the checkbox *Stock* and then choose *Material: Show Transparent and Show Part comparison* to see stock and additional details. *Click* on the *Close* button and go back to the *CAM* menu. Save the Inventor file that now includes *3D* machining *Radial1* CAM simulation.

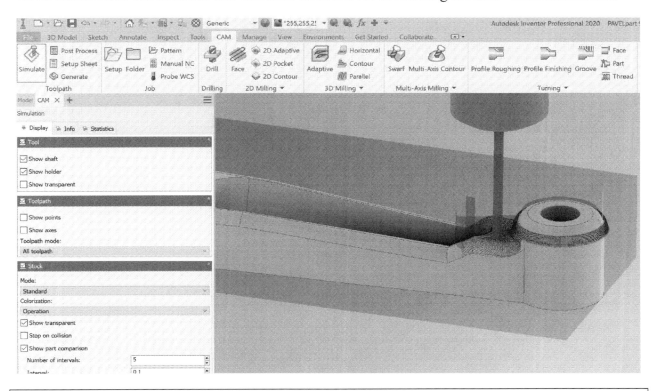

Post Processing

Now we are ready to create the CNC program. Select the operation click on the *Post Processor* on the top of the menu tab. Click on the pulldown menu and Select FANUC/Fanuc (next to Open Config button). In the *Program name or number* slot, change the program to 1037 or the desired number. Remember the numbers and where you saved your program.

A new window *Autodesk Edit CAM (HSM) Edit* pops up with your A new program inside. If the *Backplot* is selected, the postprocessor simulation window shows on the right.

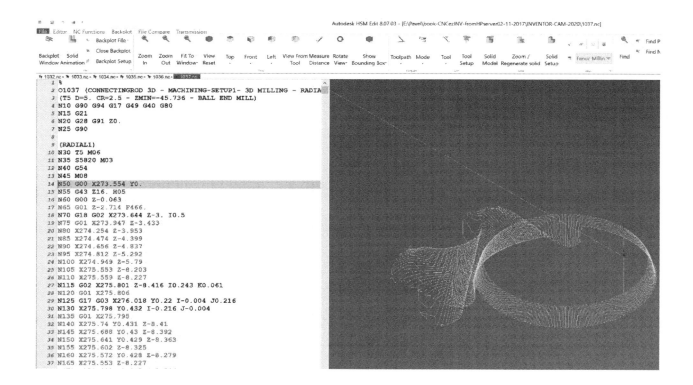

```
1  %
2  O1037 (CONNECTINGROD 3D - MACHINING-SETUP1- 3D MILLING - RADIA
3  (T5 D=5. CR=2.5 - ZMIN=-45.736 - BALL END MILL)
4  N10 G90 G94 G17 G49 G40 G80
5  N15 G21
6  N20 G28 G91 Z0.
7  N25 G90
8
9  (RADIAL1)
10 N30 T5 M06
11 N35 S5820 M03
12 N40 G54
13 N45 M08
14 N50 G00 X273.554 Y0.
15 N55 G43 Z16. H05
16 N60 G00 Z-0.063
17 N65 G01 Z-2.714 F466.
18 N70 G18 G02 X273.644 Z-3. I0.5
19 N75 G01 X273.947 Z-3.433
20 N80 X274.254 Z-3.953
21 N85 X274.474 Z-4.399
22 N90 X274.656 Z-4.837
23 N95 X274.812 Z-5.292
24 N100 X274.949 Z-5.79
25 N105 X275.553 Z-8.203
26 N110 X275.553 Z-8.227
27 N115 G02 X275.801 Z-8.416 I0.243 K0.061
28 N120 G01 X275.806
29 N125 G17 G03 X276.018 Y0.22 I-0.004 J0.216
30 N130 X275.798 Y0.432 I-0.216 J-0.004
31 N135 G01 X275.795
32 N140 X275.74 Y0.431 Z-8.41
33 N145 X275.688 Y0.43 Z-8.392
34 N150 X275.641 Y0.429 Z-8.363
35 N155 X275.602 Z-8.325
36 N160 X275.572 Y0.428 Z-8.279
37 N165 X275.553 Z-8.227
```

206

3D Spiral

In *3D Milling, Spiral* is used for finishing milling processes; it is starting from a center point and created spiral toolpath. From pulldown menu select *spiral*, a new *Spiral*: sub-window appears with several tabs, the first is the *Tool*. We need to select a tool from the library. In the right window, select the tool **#5-∅5mm ball (Ball Mill)**, the same one we used in the previous operation, and finish by clicking *Select* on the bottom right. The new tool is selected, and its number and size appear next to *Tool: #5-∅5mm ball (5 mm Ball Endmill)*.

Next on the *Geometry* tap select Machining boundary: Silhouette, and click on the center point of the big cylinder, to machine other surfaces outside the cylinder, select and modify *Additional offset: 2mm*. Select the *Passes* tab and modify *Stepover: 1 mm*, to make smoother machining. The rest of the tabs *Height,* and *Linking* will not be altered for this operation.

Complete this operation by clicking on *OK* on the bottom of the right sub-window. Now the A new operation *[T5] Spiral1* is created under the *Setup1*. It has submenus Tool number, WCS, and size of the program in bytes. If you select on the [5] *Spiral1,* the tool path profile (blue/green lines) will show on the main window.

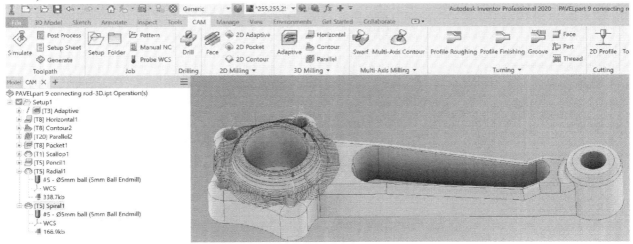

We can simulate all the *3D Spiral1* process by selecting *Simulate* on the main tab. A new simulation window pops up, and the control buttons are the same as described above. You can select the checkbox *Stock* and then choose *Material: Show Transparent and Show Part comparison* to see stock and additional details. *Click* on the *Close* button and go back to the *CAM* menu. Save the Inventor file that now includes *3D* machining *Spiral1* CAM simulation.

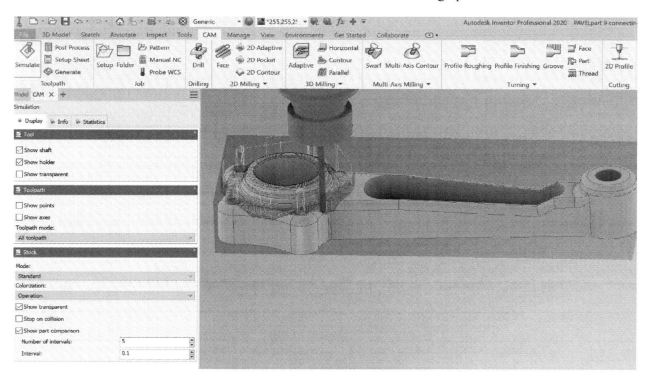

Now we are ready to create the CNC program. Select the operation click on the *Post Processor* on the top of the menu tab. Click on the pulldown menu and Select FANUC/Fanuc (next to Open Config button). In the *Program name or number* slot, change the program to 1038 or the desired number. Remember the numbers and where you saved your program.

A new window *Autodesk Edit CAM (HSM) Edit* pops up with your A new program inside. If the *Backplot* is selected, the postprocessor simulation window shows on the right.

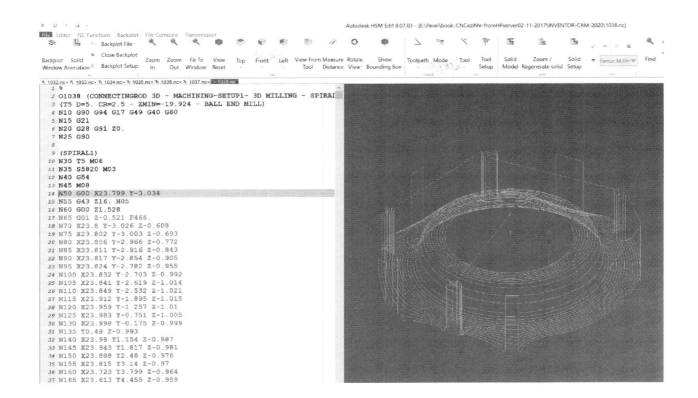

```
1  %
2  O1038 (CONNECTINGROD 3D - MACHINING-SETUP1- 3D MILLING - SPIRA
3  (T5 D=5. CR=2.5 - ZMIN=-19.924 - BALL END MILL)
4  N10 G90 G94 G17 G49 G40 G80
5  N15 G21
6  N20 G28 G91 Z0.
7  N25 G90
8
9  (SPIRAL1)
10 N30 T5 M06
11 N35 S5820 M03
12 N40 G54
13 N45 M08
14 N50 G00 X23.799 Y-3.034
15 N55 G43 Z16. H05
16 N60 G00 Z1.528
17 N65 G01 Z-0.521 F466.
18 N70 X23.8 Y-3.026 Z-0.608
19 N75 X23.802 Y-3.003 Z-0.693
20 N80 X23.806 Y-2.966 Z-0.772
21 N85 X23.811 Y-2.916 Z-0.843
22 N90 X23.817 Y-2.854 Z-0.905
23 N95 X23.824 Y-2.782 Z-0.955
24 N100 X23.832 Y-2.703 Z-0.992
25 N105 X23.841 Y-2.619 Z-1.014
26 N110 X23.849 Y-2.532 Z-1.021
27 N115 X23.912 Y-1.895 Z-1.015
28 N120 X23.959 Y-1.257 Z-1.01
29 N125 X23.983 Y-0.751 Z-1.005
30 N130 X23.998 Y-0.175 Z-0.999
31 N135 Y0.49 Z-0.993
32 N140 X23.98 Y1.154 Z-0.987
33 N145 X23.943 Y1.817 Z-0.981
34 N150 X23.888 Y2.48 Z-0.976
35 N155 X23.815 Y3.14 Z-0.97
36 N160 X23.723 Y3.799 Z-0.964
37 N165 X23.613 Y4.455 Z-0.959
```

209

3D Morphed Spiral

In *3D Milling,* the *Morphed Spiral* process is similar to the *Spiral,* but the path is generated from the selected boundary, which provides smoother finishing toolpath for free form surfaces. From pulldown menu select *Morphed Spiral*, a new *Morphed Spiral2:* sub-window appears with several tabs, the first is the *Tool.* We need to select a tool from the library. In the right window, select the tool **#5-Ø5mm ball (Ball Mill)**, the same one we used in the previous operation, and finish by clicking *Select* on the bottom right. The new tool is selected, and its number and size appear next to *Tool: #5-Ø5mm ball (5 mm Ball Endmill).*

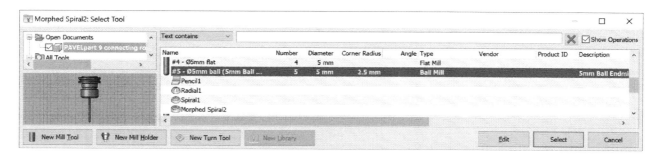

Next on the *Geometry* tap select *Machining boundary: Selection,* and click on the surface you want to machine. The rest of tabs *Height,* Passes, and *Linking* will not be altered for this operation.

Complete this operation by clicking on *OK* on the bottom of the right sub-window. Now the A new operation *[T5] Morphed Spiral2* is created under the *Setup1.* It has submenus Tool number, WCS, and size of the program in bytes. If you select on the [5] *Morphed Spiral2,* the tool path profile (blue/green lines) will show on the main window. Notice the difference how the toolpath follow the profile.

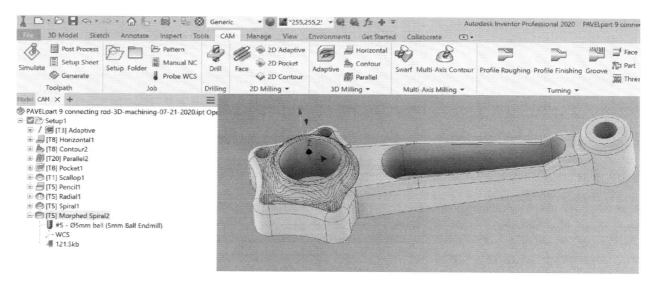

We can simulate the *3D Morphed Spiral2* process by selecting *Simulate* on the main tab. A new simulation window pops up, and the control buttons are the same as described above. You can select the checkbox *Stock* and then choose *Material: Show Transparent and Show Part comparison* to see stock and additional details. *Click* on the *Close* button and go back to the *CAM* menu. Save the Inventor file that now includes *3D* machining *Morphed Spiral2* CAM simulation.

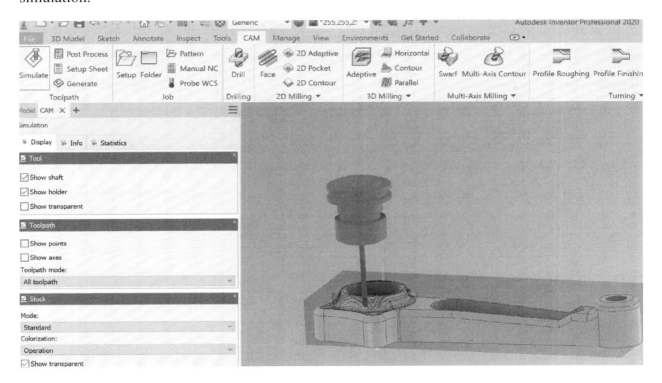

Now we are ready to create the CNC program. Select the operation click on the *Post Processor* on the top of the menu tab. Click on the pulldown menu and Select FANUC/Fanuc (next to Open Config button). In the *Program name or number* slot, change the program to 1039 or the desired number. Remember the numbers and where you saved your program.

A new window *Autodesk Edit CAM (HSM) Edit* pops up with your A new program inside. If the *Backplot* is selected, the postprocessor simulation window shows on the right.

Backplot File ·
Close Backplot
Backplot Solid   Backplot Setup   Zoom Zoom Fit To   View   Top   Front Left   View From Measure Rotate   Show   Toolpath Mode   Tool   Tool   Solid   Zoom /   Solid   Fenuc Millin   Find
Window Animation   In   Out   Window Reset   Tool   Distance View Bounding Box   Setup   Model Regenerate solid Setup

```
1 %
2 O1039 (CONNECTINGROD 3D - MACHINING-SETUP1- 3D MILLING - MORPHE
3 (T5 D=5. CR=2.5 - ZMIN=-46.25 - BALL END MILL)
4 N10 G90 G94 G17 G49 G40 G80
5 N15 G21
6 N20 G28 G91 Z0.
7 N25 G90
8
9 (MORPHED SPIRAL2)
10 N30 T5 M06
11 N35 S5820 M03
12 N40 G54
13 N45 M08
14 N50 G00 X0.5 Y26.01
15 N55 G43 Z16. H05
16 N60 G00 Z2.
17 N65 G01 Z0.5 F466.
18 N70 X0.492 Z0.413
19 N75 X0.47 Y26.009 Z0.329
20 N80 X0.433 Y26.008 Z0.25
21 N85 X0.383 Y26.007 Z0.179
22 N90 X0.321 Y26.006 Z0.117
23 N95 X0.25 Y26.005 Z0.067
24 N100 X0.171 Y26.003 Z0.03
25 N105 X0.087 Y26.002 Z0.008
26 N110 X0. Y26. Z0.
27 N115 X-1.014 Y25.98
28 N120 X-2.027 Y25.921
29 N125 X-3.067 Y25.818
30 N130 X-4.042 Y25.684
31 N135 X-5.07 Y25.5
32 N140 X-6.033 Y25.291
33 N145 X-7.015 Y25.036
34 N150 X-8.023 Y24.73
35 N155 X-8.945 Y24.413
36 N160 X-9.93 Y24.028
37 N165 X-10.822 Y23.641
```

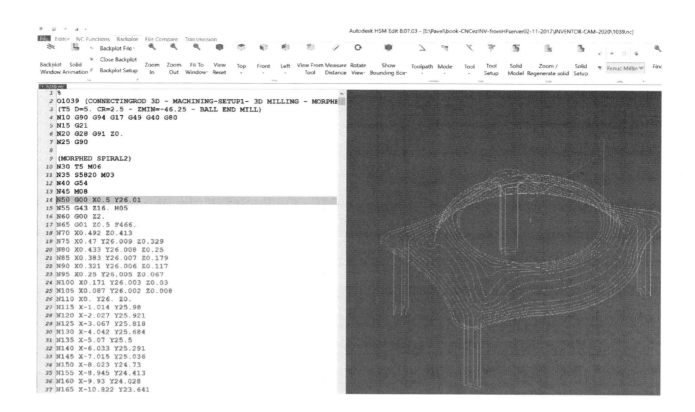

212

3D Ramp

In *3D Milling, Ramp* is used for finishing toolpath for steep walls. It similar to the *Contour,* but the path is ramped down instead to machine at constant Z depths. From the pulldown menu *Ramp*, a new *Ramp1*: sub-window appears with several tabs; the first is the *Tool*. We need to select a tool from the library. In the right window, select the tool **#5-Ø5mm ball (Ball Mill)**, the same one we used in the previous operation, and finish by clicking *Select* on the bottom right. The new tool is selected, and its number and size appear next to *Tool: #5-Ø5mm ball (5 mm Ball Endmill)*.

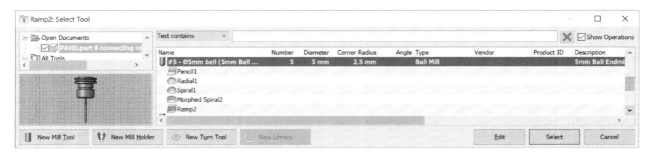

Next on the *Geometry* tap select *Machining boundary: Selection* and click on the edge of the surface you want to machine, for example, click on the top edge of the big middle slot. The rest of tabs *Height,* Passes, and *Linking* will not be altered for this operation.

Complete this operation by clicking on *OK* on the bottom of the right sub-window. Now the A new operation *[T5] Ramp2* is created under the *Setup1*. It has submenus Tool number, WCS, and size of the program in bytes. If you select on the [5] *Ramp2,* the tool path profile (blue/green lines) will show on the main window.

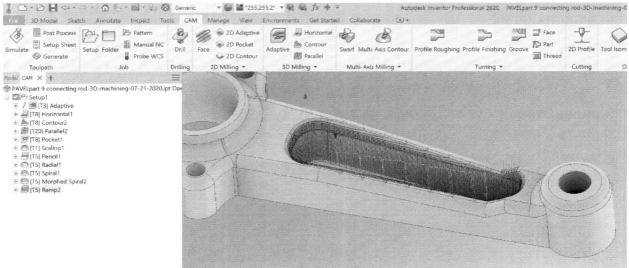

We can simulate the *3D Ramp2* process by selecting *Simulate* on the main tab. A new simulation window pops up, and the control buttons are the same as described above. You can select the checkbox *Stock* and then choose *Material: Show Transparent and Show Part comparison* to see stock and additional details. *Click* on the *Close* button and go back to the *CAM* menu. Save the Inventor file that now includes *3D* machining *Ramp2* CAM simulation.

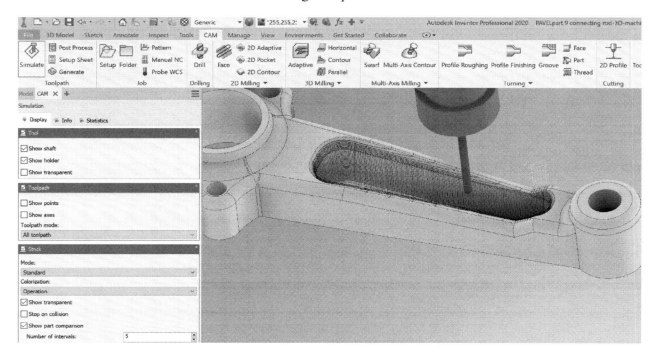

Now we are ready to create the CNC program. Select the operation click on the *Post Processor* on the top of the menu tab. Click on the pulldown menu and Select FANUC/Fanuc (next to Open Config button). In the *Program name or number* slot, change the program to 1040 or the desired number. Remember the numbers and where you saved your program.

A new window *Autodesk Edit CAM (HSM) Edit* pops up with your A new program inside. If the *Backplot* is selected, the postprocessor simulation window shows on the right.

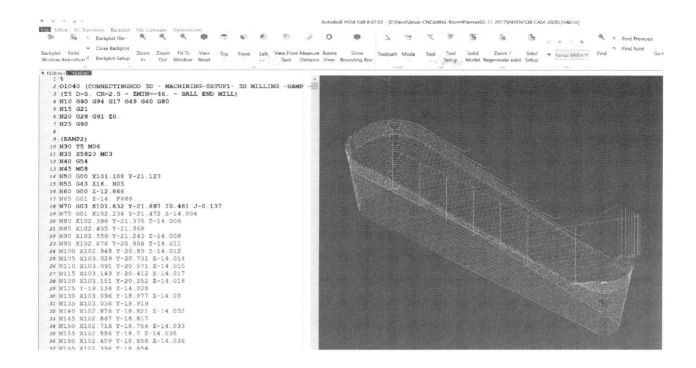

```
1  %
2  O1040 (CONNECTINGROD 3D - MACHINING-SETUP1- 3D MILLING -RAMP -
3  (T5 D=5. CR=2.5 - ZMIN=-46. - BALL END MILL)
4  N10 G90 G94 G17 G49 G40 G80
5  N15 G21
6  N20 G28 G91 Z0.
7  N25 G90
8
9  (RAMP2)
10 N30 T5 M06
11 N35 S5820 M03
12 N40 G54
13 N45 M08
14 N50 G00 X101.108 Y-21.123
15 N55 G43 Z16. H05
16 N60 G00 Z-12.866
17 N65 G01 Z-14. F466.
18 N70 G03 X101.832 Y-21.697 I0.481 J-0.137
19 N75 G01 X102.236 Y-21.472 Z-14.004
20 N80 X102.396 Y-21.375 Z-14.006
21 N85 X102.405 Y-21.369
22 N90 X102.556 Y-21.243 Z-14.008
23 N95 X102.876 Y-20.958 Z-14.011
24 N100 X102.945 Y-20.89 Z-14.012
25 N105 X103.029 Y-20.731 Z-14.014
26 N110 X103.091 Y-20.571 Z-14.015
27 N115 X103.149 Y-20.412 Z-14.017
28 N120 X103.151 Y-20.252 Z-14.018
29 N125 Y-19.136 Z-14.028
30 N130 X103.096 Y-18.977 Z-14.03
31 N135 X103.036 Y-18.919
32 N140 X102.876 Y-18.821 Z-14.032
33 N145 X102.867 Y-18.817
34 N150 X102.716 Y-18.754 Z-14.033
35 N155 X102.556 Y-18.7 Z-14.035
36 N160 X102.409 Y-18.658 Z-14.036
37 N165 X102.396 Y-18.654
```

3D Project

In the *3D Milling, Project* is a process for machining contours or lines with the tool center part. This process is often used for text or linear path engraving onto a surface. The contours can be created on the same or other surfaces. Let create a simple contour on one plane, as shown below.

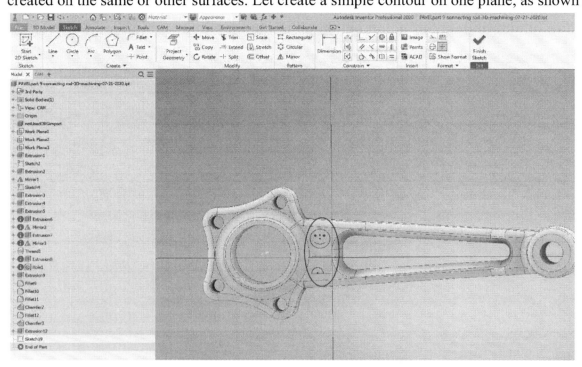

From the pulldown menu select *Project* menu, a new *Project2*: sub-window appears with several tabs; the first is the *Tool*. Since the operation is for 3D machining, we will select a new chamfer tool. Select *Sample Library → Tutorial-Metric*, then on the right window select tool **Ø10mm 45⁰ chamfer (Chamfer Mill)** and finish by clicking *Select* on the bottom right. The new tool is selected, and its number and size appear next to *Tool: #50- Ø10mm 45⁰ chamfer.*

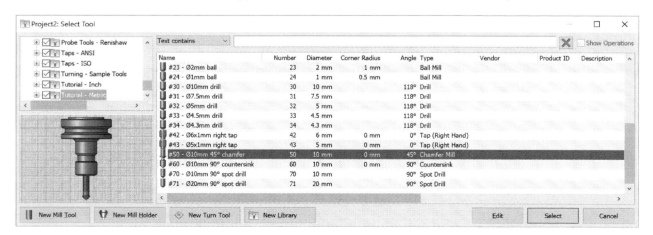

Next on the *Geometry* tap select *Contour selection* and click on each contour (hold Shift if needed) you created in the sketch or select the sketch from the *Model* tab. The tabs *Height, Passes,* and *Linking* will not be altered for this operation.

Complete this operation by clicking on *OK* on the bottom of the right sub-window. Now a new operation [*T50] Project2* is created under the *Setup1*. It has submenus Tool number, WCS, and size of the program in bytes. If you select the *#50- Ø10mm 45⁰ chamfer,* the tool path profile (blue/green lines) will show on the main window.

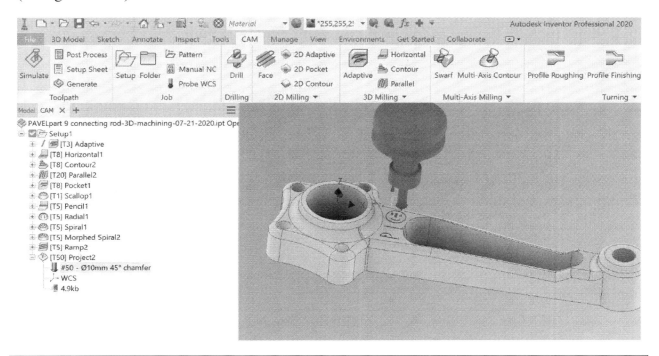

Simulation

We can simulate all the *3D Project2* process by selecting *Simulate* on the main tab. A new simulation window pops up, and the control buttons are the same as described above. You can select the checkbox *Stock* and then choose *Material: Show Transparent and Show Part comparison* to see stock and additional details. *Click* on the *Close* button and go back to the *CAM* menu. Save the Inventor file that now includes *3D* machining *Pencil1* CAM simulation.

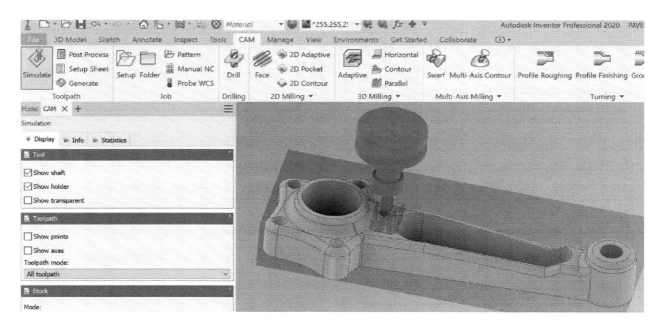

Post Processing

Now we are ready to create the CNC program. Select the operation click on the *Post Processor* on the top of the menu tab. Click on the pulldown menu and Select FANUC/Fanuc (next to Open Config button). In the *Program name or number* slot, change the program to 1041 or the desired number. Remember the numbers and where you saved your program.

A new window *Autodesk Edit CAM (HSM) Edit* pops up with your A new program inside. If the *Backplot* is selected, the postprocessor simulation window shows on the right.

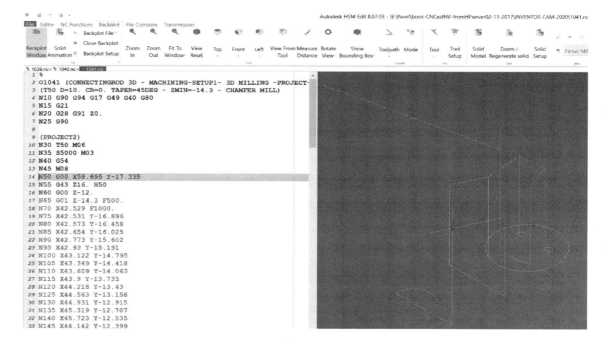

3D Morph

3D Milling Morph is finishing toolpath for shallow zones between contours. From the pulldown menu select *Morph*, a new *Morph2*: sub-window appears with several tabs, the first is the *Tool*. We need to select a tool from the library. In the right window, select the tool **#20-Ø10mm ball (Ball Mill)**, the same one used in the previous operation, and finish by clicking *Select* on the bottom right. The new tool is selected, and its number and size appear next to *Tool: #20-Ø10mm ball (10 mm Ball Endmill)*.

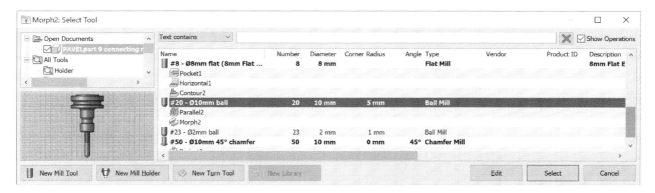

Next on the *Geometry* tap select *Curve Selection: Silhouette*, and click on click on the edge of the surface you want to machine. The rest of tabs *Height,* Passes, and *Linking* will not be altered for this operation.

Complete this operation by clicking on *OK* on the bottom of the right sub-window. Now the A new operation *[T20] Morph2* is created under the *Setup1*. It has submenus Tool number, WCS, and size of the program in bytes. If you select the *[T20] Morph2,* the tool path profile (blue/green lines) will show on the main window. Notice the difference in how the toolpath follows the profile.

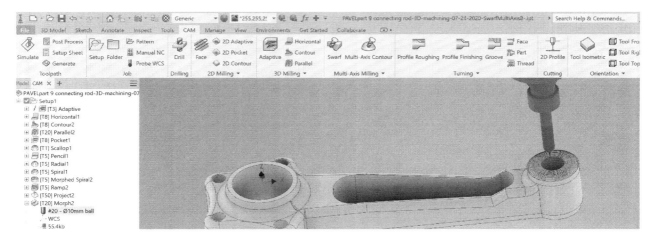

We can simulate all the *3D Morph2* process by selecting *Simulate* on the main tab. A new simulation window pops up, and the control buttons are the same as described above. You can select the checkbox *Stock* and then choose *Material: Show Transparent and Show Part comparison* to see stock and additional details. *Click* on the *Close* button and go back to the *CAM* menu. Save the Inventor file that now includes *3D* machining *Morph2* CAM simulation.

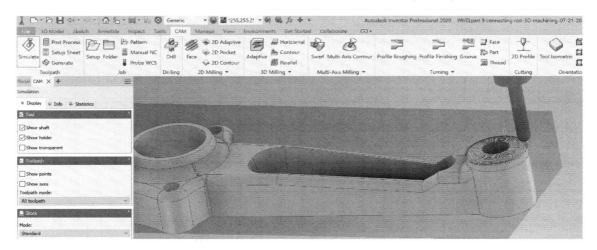

Post Processing

Now we are ready to create the CNC program. Select the operation click on the *Post Processor* on the top of the menu tab, select FANUC/Fanuc, change the program to 1042 or the desired number. A new window *Autodesk Edit CAM (HSM) Edit* pops up with your new program inside. If the *Backplot* is selected, the postprocessor simulation window shows on the right.

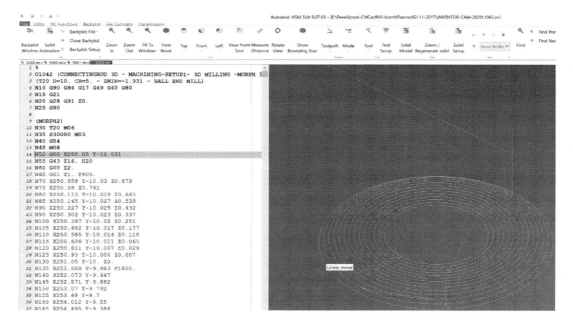

3D Flow

3D Milling Flow is finishing toolpath following ISO parametric curves of surfaces. From the pulldown menu, select *Flow*, a new *Flow1*: sub-window appears with several tabs, the first is the *Tool*. We need to select a tool from the library. In the right window, select the tool **#5-Ø5mm ball (Ball Mill)**, the same one we used in the previous operation, and finish by clicking *Select* on the bottom right. The new tool is selected, and its number and size appear next to *Tool: #5-Ø5mm ball (5 mm Ball Endmill)*.

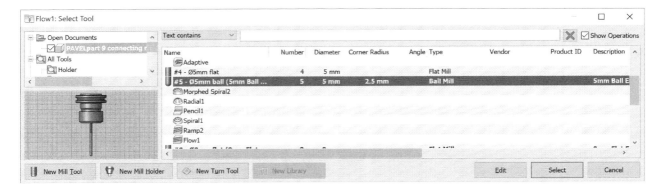

Next on the *Geometry* tap select *Geometry*, and click on the surfaces you want to machine. Select *Passes* tab and modify the *Number of stepovers: 7* or desired number of steps. The rest of the tabs *Height* and *Linking* will not be altered for this operation.

Complete this operation by clicking on *OK* on the bottom of the right sub-window. Now a new operation *[T5] Flow1* is created under the *Setup1*. It has submenus Tool number, WCS, and size of the program in bytes. If you select the *[T5] Flow1,* the tool path profile (blue/green lines) will show on the main window.

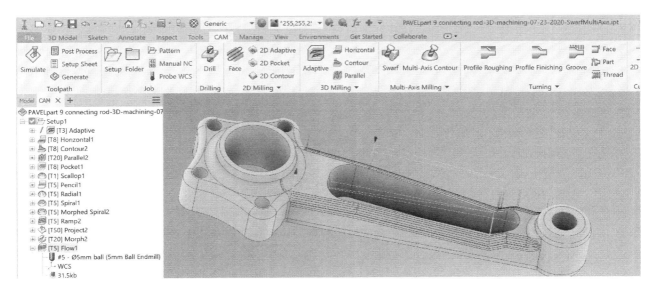

We can simulate all the *Flow1* process by selecting *Simulate* on the main tab. A new simulation window pops up, and the control buttons are the same as described above. You can select the checkbox *Stock* and then choose *Material: Show Transparent and Show Part comparison* to see stock and additional details. *Click* on the *Close* button and go back to the *CAM* menu. Save the Inventor file that now includes 3D machining *Morph2* CAM simulation.

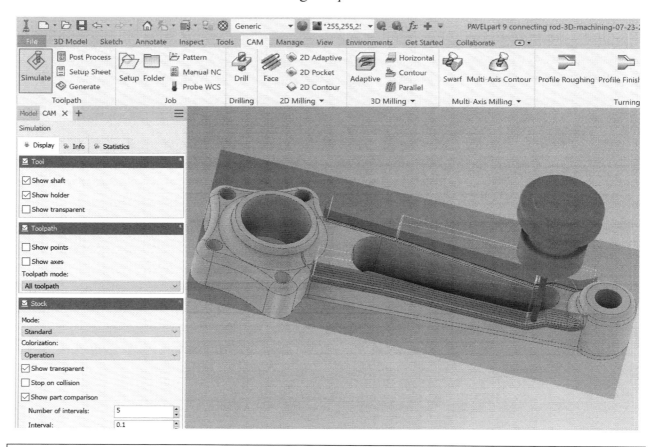

Post Processing

Now we are ready to create the CNC program. Select the operation click on the *Post Processor* on the top of the menu tab. Click on the pulldown menu and Select FANUC/Fanuc (next to Open Config button). In the *Program name or number* slot, change the program to 1043 or the desired number. Remember the numbers and where you saved your program.

A new window *Autodesk Edit CAM (HSM) Edit* pops up with your A new program inside. If the *Backplot* is selected, the postprocessor simulation window shows on the right.

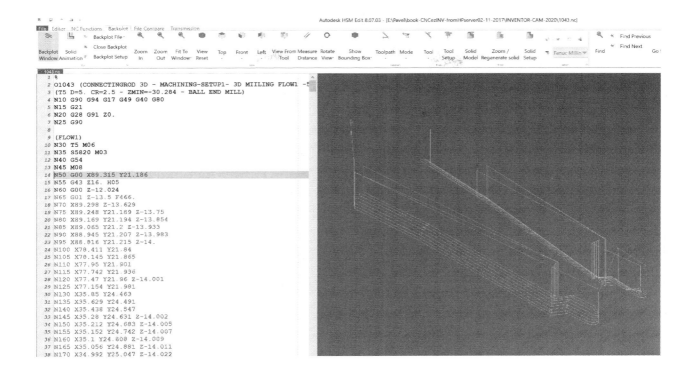

Notes:

Notes:

Chapter 9

CNC Programming with Inventor CAM:

Multi-axis Machining

Inventor Multi-Axis Milling

Multi-Axis Milling is advance simultaneous machining involving 4, 5, or more tool path method. There are many parts with complex curvilinear surfaces with cavities and small radii that are difficult to reach when using small diameter tools.

Swarf

Swarf is *Multi-Axis Milling* that uses the side of the tool for cutting. From the pulldown menu select *Swarf*, a new *Swarf1:* sub-window appears with several tabs, the first is the *Tool*. We need to choose a tool from the library. In the right window, select the tool **#8-Ø8mm flat (Flat End Mill)**, we used in one of the previous operations, and finish by clicking *Select* on the bottom right. The new tool is selected, and its number and size appear next to *Tool: #8-Ø8mm flat (Flat End Mill)*.

Next on the *Geometry* tap from *Drive mode:* select *Surfaces,* and click on the surfaces you want to machine. For example, we will machine the designed fillets (short inclined surfaces) on the bottom side of the part. Notice that the coordinate orientation from the Setup1 has Z-axis pointing away from the machined surface. We can create a new setup to change the coordinate system or use the existing one. Instead, we will use something different. Inventor CAM has a great capability to select the tool orientation that will modify the coordinate system orientation to point out toward tool direction. In the *Geometry* tab, click on *Tool orientation*: and from the pulldown menu select *Select Z axis/plane & X axis* and click on the bottom surface. You can choose other tool orientation options if this one doesn't work for you. Next, in the Passes tab, check the Manual stepdowns and modify, Number of stepdowns: 3, Maximum stepdown: 2mm, to make more steps. The rest of tabs Height and Linking will no be altered for this operation.

Complete this operation by clicking on *OK* on the bottom of the right sub-window. Now the new operation *[T8] Swarf1* is created under the *Setup1*. It has submenus Tool number, WCS, and size of the program in bytes. If you select the *[T8] Swarf1*, the tool path profile (blue/green lines) will show on the main window. Notice the axis and tool orientation has changed and how the toolpath follows the profile.

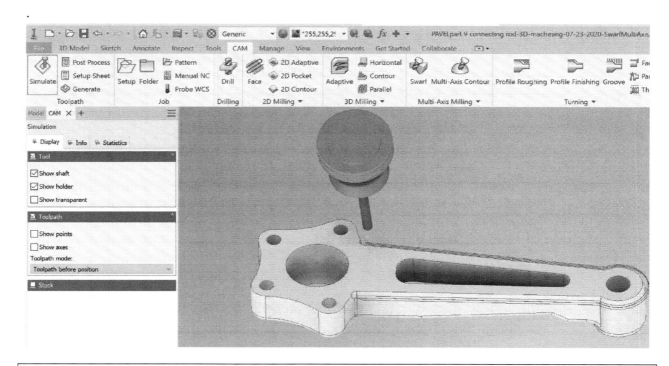

Simulation

We can simulate all the *Swarf1* process by selecting *Simulate* on the main tab. A new simulation window pops up, and the control buttons are the same as described above. You can select the checkbox *Stock* and then choose *Material: Show Transparent and Show Part comparison* to see stock and additional details. Notice how the tool tilts when following the profile. Click on the *Close* button and go back to the *CAM* menu. Save the Inventor file that now includes *Swarf1* CAM simulation.

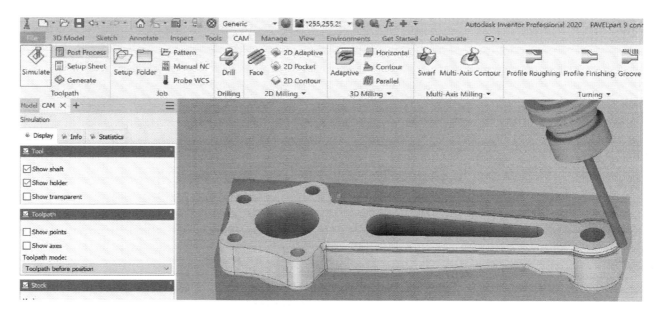

Now we are ready to create the CNC program. Select the operation click on the *Post Processor* on the top of the menu tab. Click on the pulldown menu and Select FANUC/Fanuc (next to Open Config button). In the *Program name or number* slot, change the program to 1050 or the desired number. Remember the numbers and where you saved your program.

A new window *Autodesk Edit CAM (HSM) Edit* pops up with your new program inside. If the *Backplot* is selected, the postprocessor simulation window shows on the right.

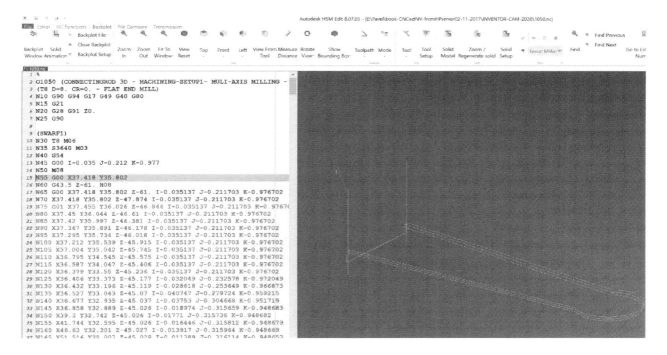

Multi-Axis Contour

Multi-Axis Contour is *Multi-Axis Milling* that uses the tip of the tool fooling contour of a 3D curve. The tool is kept normal to the cutting surface. Additional control of the contact points can be provided by inclining the tool in the desired direction and/or using compensation on the left, right, or center. From *Multi-Axis Milling* menu select *Multi-Axis Contour*, a new *Multi-Axis Contour1:* sub-window appears with several tabs, the first is the *Tool*. We need to select a tool from the library. In the right window, select the tool **#5-Ø5mm ball (Ball Endmill)**, the same one we used in one of the previous operations, and finish by clicking *Select* on the bottom right. The new tool is selected, and its number and size appear next to *Tool: #5-Ø5mm ball (Ball Endmill)*.

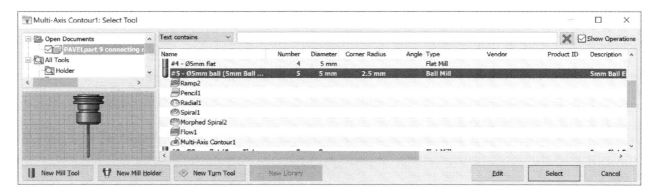

Next on the *Geometry* tap, select *Curve selection:* and click on the edges you want to machine. For example, we can machine the smallest fillets on the sidewall and curvilinear edges of the fillet in front of the smaller cylinder. Coordinate orientation from the Setup1 has the Z-axis pointing away from the machined surface. Again instead of creating a new setup to change the coordinate system, we will use Inventor CAM capability to select the tool orientation that will modify the coordinate system orientation to point out toward tool direction. In the *Geometry* tab, click on *Tool orientation:* and from the pulldown menu select *Select Z axis/plane & X axis* and select flat surface inside the slot to make Z-axis pointing on the slot direction, away from the big cylinder. You can choose other tool orientation options if this one doesn't work for you. The rest of tabs *Height, Passes,* and *Linking* will not be altered for this operation.

Complete this operation by clicking on *OK* on the bottom of the right sub-window. Now the new operation *[T5] Multi-Axis Contour1* is created under the *Setup1*. It has submenus Tool number, WCS, and size of the program in bytes. If you select the *[T5] Multi-Axis Contour1*, the tool path profile (blue/green lines) will show on the main window. Notice how the axis, and tool orientation has changed and the toolpath follows the curvilinear profiles.

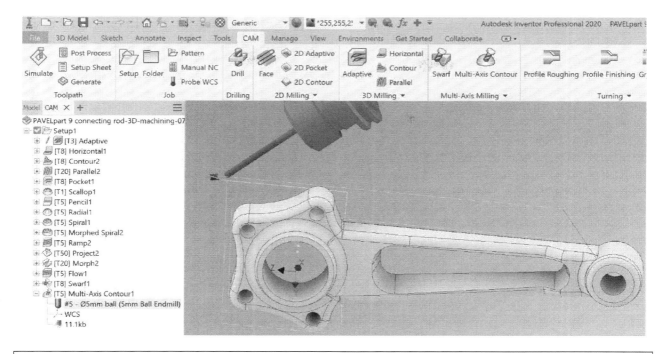

Simulation

We can simulate all the *Multi-Axis Contour1* process by selecting *Simulate* on the main tab. A new simulation window pops up, and the control buttons are the same as described above. You can select he checkbox *Stock* and then choose *Material: Show Transparent and Show Part comparison* to see stock and additional details. Notice how the tool tilts when following the profile. Click on the *Close* button and go back to the *CAM* menu. Save the Inventor file that now includes *Multi-Axis Contour1* CAM simulation.

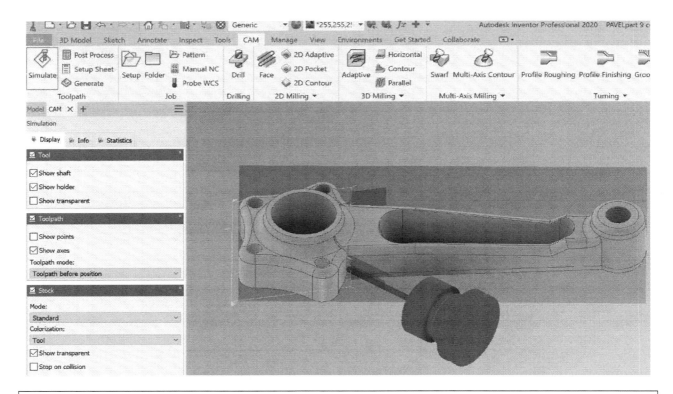

Post Processing

Now we are ready to create the CNC program. Select the operation click on the *Post Processor* on the top of the menu tab. Click on the pulldown menu and Select FANUC/Fanuc (next to Open Config button). In the *Program name or number* slot, change the program to 1051 or the desired number. Remember the numbers and where you saved your program.

A new window *Autodesk Edit CAM (HSM) Edit* pops up with your new program inside. If the *Backplot* is selected, the postprocessor simulation window shows on the right.

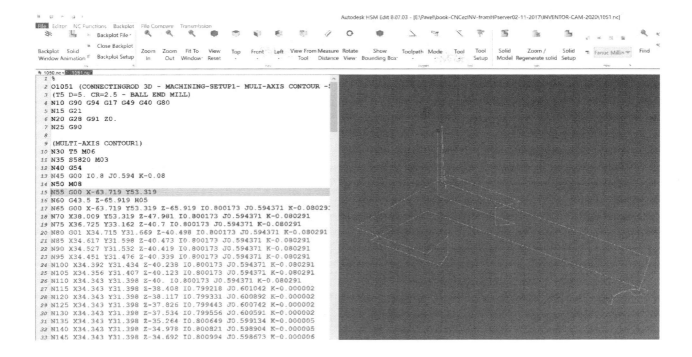

```
1  %
2  O1051 (CONNECTINGROD 3D - MACHINING-SETUP1- MULI-AXIS CONTOUR -5
3  (T5 D=5. CR=2.5 - BALL END MILL)
4  N10 G90 G94 G17 G49 G40 G80
5  N15 G21
6  N20 G28 G91 Z0.
7  N25 G90
8
9  (MULTI-AXIS CONTOUR1)
10 N30 T5 M06
11 N35 S5820 M03
12 N40 G54
13 N45 G00 I0.8 J0.594 K-0.08
14 N50 M08
15 N55 G00 X-63.719 Y53.319
16 N60 G43.5 Z-65.919 H05
17 N65 G00 X-63.719 Y53.319 Z-65.919 I0.800173 J0.594371 K-0.08029
18 N70 X38.009 Y53.319 Z-47.981 I0.800173 J0.594371 K-0.080291
19 N75 X36.725 Y33.162 Z-40.7 I0.800173 J0.594371 K-0.080291
20 N80 G01 X34.715 Y31.669 Z-40.498 I0.800173 J0.594371 K-0.080291
21 N85 X34.617 Y31.598 Z-40.473 I0.800173 J0.594371 K-0.080291
22 N90 X34.527 Y31.532 Z-40.419 I0.800173 J0.594371 K-0.080291
23 N95 X34.451 Y31.476 Z-40.339 I0.800173 J0.594371 K-0.080291
24 N100 X34.392 Y31.434 Z-40.238 I0.800173 J0.594371 K-0.080291
25 N105 X34.356 Y31.407 Z-40.123 I0.800173 J0.594371 K-0.080291
26 N110 X34.343 Y31.398 Z-40. I0.800173 J0.594371 K-0.080291
27 N115 X34.343 Y31.398 Z-38.408 I0.799218 J0.601042 K-0.000002
28 N120 X34.343 Y31.398 Z-38.117 I0.799331 J0.600892 K-0.000002
29 N125 X34.343 Y31.398 Z-37.826 I0.799443 J0.600742 K-0.000002
30 N130 X34.343 Y31.398 Z-37.534 I0.799556 J0.600591 K-0.000002
31 N135 X34.343 Y31.398 Z-35.264 I0.800649 J0.599134 K-0.000005
32 N140 X34.343 Y31.398 Z-34.978 I0.800821 J0.598904 K-0.000005
33 N145 X34.343 Y31.398 Z-34.692 I0.800994 J0.598673 K-0.000006
```

233

Simulation of all 3D Milling and Multi-Axis Milling processes

Simulation

We can simulate all the 3D Milling and Multi-Axis Milling processes by selecting Setup1, the clicking on *Simulate* on the main tab. A new simulation window pops up, and the control buttons are the same as described above. You can select the checkbox *Stock* and then select *Material: Show Transparent and Show Part comparison* to see stock and additional details.

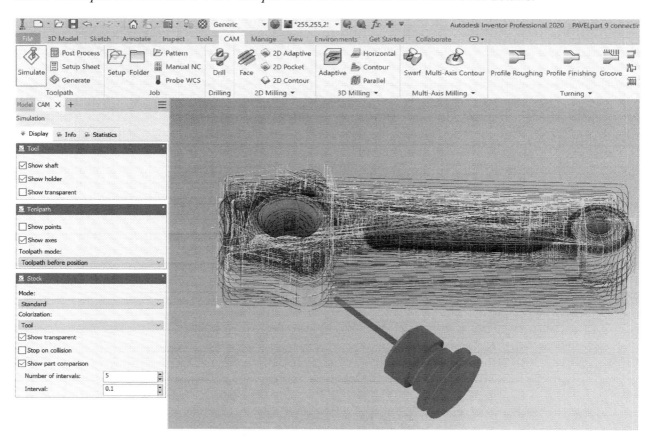

Now we are ready to create the third CNC program. Select the operation click on the *Post Processor* on the top of the menu tab. Click on the pulldown menu and Select FANUC/Fanuc (next to Open Confi button). In the *Program name or number* slot, change the program to 1055 or the desired number. Remember the numbers and where you saved your program. Click on *Post* to save the program to the desired Folder. This time we will create all machining processes in one program. Select the *Setup1* and run the on *Post Processor*, save to new program number 1055. The program will contain all operations, including all tool changes.

A new window *Autodesk Edit CAM (HSM) Edit* pops up with your new program inside. If the *Backlot* is selected, the postprocessor simulation window shows on the right.

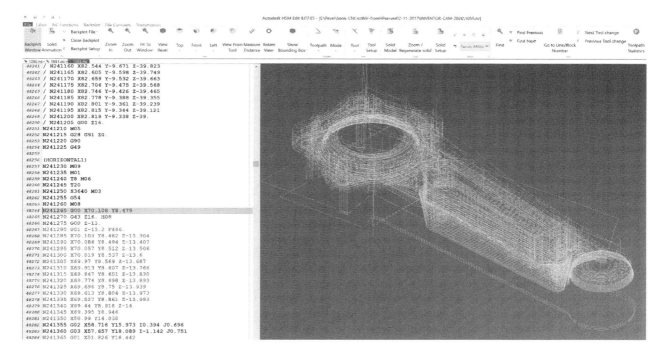

This concludes 3D Milling and Multi-Axis Milling

Notes:

Notes:

Glossary

A Axis - A rotary axis around the X axis

Absolute - Tooltip positions programmed relative to an origin (zero) point of the workpiece. G90 is the code used for absolute positioning.

Absolute dimensioning - All workpiece dimensions are calculated relative to a fixed origin.

Address - A letter or group of letters and/or numbers in G and M mode defining a class of functions. Z1.5 the address code Z with it 1.5 is a coordinate value for the Z axis.

ANSI - American National Standards Institute a private non-profit organization that oversees the development of voluntary consensus national, regional, international standards for products, services, processes, systems, and personnel in the USA.

APT - Automatically Programmed Tools. Used to program CNC machines tools paths for complex shapes. APT was the first and remains today the powerful computer-aided part programming language. It runs on computers and can be used for four- and five-axis machining of complex part surfaces.

ASCII (American Standard Code for Information Interchange) - A standard format for the interexchange textual data between computer systems. I uses 7 or 8 bits; each bit can have value 0 or 1, allowing different combinations - 128 (for 7 bit) or 256 (for 8 bit). Each combination represents one character. For example, 01111010 would represent the letter z.

Auxiliary Functions - Functions like coolant on/off, spindle on/off, and pallet change.

Axis - A Fixed reference line of a coordinate system. In CNC term, specifies coordinates and direction of the moving tool on the X, Y, and Z axes.

B axis - A rotary axis around the Y axis.

Backplot - Simplified graphical representations, on the computer screen, of the CNC program toolpath, used to verify the CNC part program.

Binary code - Represents text, computer processor instructions, or other data using any two-symbol system binary digits (0 or 1). It is the internal code the computer operates on.

Block - One line of a CNC program representing operational instruction. The CNC executes one block at the time and moves sequentially to the next block. Each block is ended by an end-of-block (EOB) character.

Block Number - The line number at the beginning of each block can be used to control the flow of the CNC program when used canned cycle, or subroutines, it also makes it easy for the operator to follow the program structure and flow.

Block skip - A backslash (/) entered in the front of any block causes the CNC system to ignore this block in a program. Block skip is also called Block delete.

Byte - 8 bits. It can represent numbers from 0 to 255.

C axis - A rotary axis around the Z axis.

CAD - Computer-Aided Design.

CAD/CAM- Computer-Aided Design/Computer-Aided Manufacturing.

CAE - Computer-Aided Engineering - Computer software that is used for engineering of complex components, simulations, and systems. It includes one or all of CAD, components for engineering analysis, simulation, and CAM.

CAM-Computer-Aided Manufacturing - Computer-aided technologies to design, automate, control, and improve manufacturing operations and processes.

Canned cycle - A single command (with predefined function and structure) that represents a sequence of commands (e. g. G00, G01, G02, G03), executed by issuing a single command. For example, a G71 code will initiate a rough turning cycle for a profile described by the G71 and program sequence, following it, for finished profile.

Cartesian coordinate system - Specifies each point uniquely in space by numerical coordinates (axes), which define the signed distance to the origin (reference position). Coordinate systems can be rectangular, with distance to perpendicular axes, or polar with distance and angel to axes.

Cartesian coordinates - Coordinates of a point in space relative to the origin of the Cartesian coordinate system.

Character - A number, letter, or symbol that is used in CNC programming. See ASCII.

Circular interpolation - A block of entered information directing the system to cut an arc or circle from/to coordinate points and radius defined in the block. It is programmed with G02 or G03. Example: G02 X1.5.Z-0.75 R0.75 F0.12.

CNC - Computer Numerical Control. Automatic program computer controlled machine.

Code - Represent information in a programming language understood by the control system of the CNC machine or computer.

Command - Controls signals for initiating a step in the execution of a program.

Communication – Software application programs that control the flow of information, through a communication device (serial port or network port), with other devices.

Computer Numerical Control - See CNC.

Constant surface speed - Controls the lathe spindle speed at the tooltip by continuously adjust the spindle RPM as diameter changes. G96 - constant surface speed command improves surface finish and life of the tool.

Control - The computer (machine control unit - MCU) that guides a CNC machine tool.

Conversational Programming - Uses an English-like programming language, easy to understand. It varies depends on the CNC control manufacturer. It uses graphics representation and menus to describe the operation, sizes, tools, and geometry and then generates the final program (G/M code or machine specific code) automatically.

Coordinate - Group of numbers indicating the distances along one or more axes from the origin of a Cartesian coordinate system.

CPU -Central processing unit of a computer. It includes the memory, logic, and arithmetic processing circuits, etc., required to run all program instructions.

Crest - The top of the thread teeth for external threads (bottom for internal threads.)

CRT - Cathode Ray Tube, also called display, similar to television display used in CNC to display programs, tools, graphics. Now days mostly LCD (Liquid Crystal Display) is used.

Cutter compensation - An automatic method, used to offset the cutting tool from the finished edge to represent the actual tool geometry with radius, not the virtual nose tip. It eliminates error providing proper cutting of machined profile. It is also called tool radius compensation or tool nose compensation.

Cutting speed - The speed in surface feet (or meters) per minute at the tip of the tool. The cutting speed is used to find the desired RPM using simple equation RPM = CS x 4/ D.

Cutting tool - Special hard material tool (high speed or carbide) that is used to remove material (drills and turning tools.)

Cycle - A sequence of operations, with a predefined structure, that is repeated several times.

Data - A representation of computer information, stored and transmitted in the form of electrical signal.

Digit - A character in any numbering system.

Direct Numerical Control (DNC) - Direct numerical control was used in the past, when NC machines' memories were quite limited, to download the programs one block at a time as the program ran at the machine. DNC is used now to connect directly any computer or device to one CNC.

Display - A visual representation of data or a physical device like a computer screen

Distributed Numerical Control (DNC) - A distribution architecture, includes a group of CNC machines, allowing them to communicate via a network with a centralized computer.

Dwell - A short period of time stopping the feed rates allowing the tool to finish completely the cutting off the surface at that position. G04 executes the waiting command defined by the amount of time in seconds.

Edit - Modifying an inputted program in the computer or CNC controller.

EIA code - G-code developed by the EIA.

EIA - Electronic Industries Alliance is a standards and trade organization of trade associations for electronics manufacturers in the United States. EIA created standards to ensure compatible and interchangeable equipment made by different manufacturers

EIA/ISO encoding - An encoding scheme that is similar to ASCII and is most commonly used on CNC controls.

Emergency Stop - These large red buttons on machines are allowing to stop all movement immediately of emergency conditions occurs.

End of Block (EOB) - The termination at the end of one line (block) of G & M code in the CNC program.

End of program - M02 miscellaneous (function) placed at the end of a program to terminate it execution.

EOB - See End-of-Block.

E-Stop - See Emergency Stop.

Feed rate - The rate of movement of the tool into the work for a particular machining operation. The feed rate is measured in inches (millimeters in ISO) per revolution or per minute.

Feed rate override - A manually adjustable switch, located on the machine control panel, which allows altering of the programmed feed rate during a cutting operation.

File - A unit of storage for a program on a computer system. Each CNC part program is stored as a separate file with a number for reference.

Finish cut - Final cut done on a workpiece to achieve the final size and surface finish.

Fixed canned cycle - See Canned Cycle.

Fixed Cycle - Also called canned cycles. See Canned Cycle.

FPM - Feet per minute.

G code – A preparatory function that executers curtain operation. G code for drilling, rough and finishing turning, canned cycle, linear or circular, absolute or incremental, rapid or feed, etc.

Imaginary tooltip - The point of intersection formed by two lines that are tangent to a tool nose radius and aligned with the major axes of a lathe. It is common to use this point in the programming for CNC turning when turning or facing since the tool cuts only in Z or X directions. When machining profile, the radius on the nose tip will cause profile errors when the tool moves simultaneously on both axis.

Incremental coordinate - Programming of a point on the profile of the workpiece is measured directly from the previous point.

Indexable - Tools with indexable inserts can be removed rotated, flipped, and reattached without changing the size and shape of the tool.

Input - All external information entered into the CNC controller. Input can be entered via punched tape, magnetic tape, memory storage, disk or keyboard on the control panel.

Interface - A connecting device that allows two or more pieces of computational devices to communicate information in both directions.

Interpolation - Precise movements of the CNC tool on different axes while keeping the tool precisely to the desired programmed path.

Jog -Jog button is used to move the X or Z axes of a machine in the positive or negative direction.

Lead - The distance the thread advance along its axis during one complete revolution (360°).

Linear interpolation - G01 command executes the movement on a straight line to a coordinate specified by X and Z with specified constant feed rate. Example G01X1.5Z-0.3F0.012

Local Area Network (LAN) - A method of connecting group of local computers to share information with each other.

Machine Control Unit (MCU) - Controls all CNC functions such as data processing, input, output, and I/O (Input/Output) interface.

Machine Reference (Zero) Point - See machine zero.

Machine zero-A reference position that is established at the machine startup. Machine zero is a hard position that is set by tripping limit switches on each axis. Machine zero position, also called home, is set by the manufacturer and can't be changed in the program.

Manual Programming - Writing G/M-code programming manually. This is different from conversational programming.

M-Code - Miscellaneous functions. Similarly, to G code, M codes set the control mode functions of a CNC machine that doesn't include tool movements. Example: M00 - program stop, M03-spindle clockwise rotation, and M08-coolant start.

Miscellaneous code (M-code) - See M-Code.

Miscellaneous Function - See M-Code.

Modal - Describes G/M codes or values that stay active within a program until changed by another one.

NC (Numerical Control) - At present, NC and CNC (Computer Numerical Control) term carried the same meaning. See CNC.

Networking - CNC and computer were connected through the network that provides not only program communications (downloading/uploading) but also possibilities to control and automate the whole manufacturing system.

Numerical Control - See NC.

Offline programming - CNC programming using a computer, not the CNC controller.

Offset - Tool Nose Radius compensation. Using radius compensation allow programming of the tool path, for turning or boring tools with actual coordinates without the need to recalculate coordinates. The offset value is kept inside the CNC controller in Tool Offset Registry Table.

Offset register - see Offset.

Optional Stop - M01 Optional Program Stop is used when a temporary stop needs to be performed during the CNC machining process.

Origin - The point of intersection of all axes. At the origin, all coordinates are zero. Origin of the part coordinate system, specified during the CNC lathe setup, is typically set at the front of the workpiece.

Part program - The instructions (program) including G/M commands, addresses, and values to produce a workpiece. The CNC machine runs the program to produce a part.

Part zero - See Origin.

Peck drilling - G75 peck drilling cycle. Drilling operations that reciprocate in and out of the drilled hole with specific parameters that allow to break chips and clear the bottom of the hole.

Perforated tape - See Tape.

Pitch - The distance between the adjacent surfaces on the pitch diameter. Often it is measured at crests or roots of thread teeth, for $60°$ degree standard thread.

Positioning (contouring) - Synchronized motion on the predefined continuous path. The continuous path system involves simultaneously control on two, three, or more axes.

Positioning (point to point) - Tool move (rapidly0 from a point to next (destination) programmed point in space, then performs an operation such as drilling, boring, tapping, reaming, and threading. The cutting operations are controlled only at the destination point.

Preparatory code - Codes that perform active machining operations or settings. See also G-code.

Preparatory function - See Preparatory code.

Program Stop - M00 program stop is used when a temporary stop needs to be performed during the CNC machining process.

Program Reference (Zero) Point - See Origin.

Rapid Linear Motion - Rapid position the tool to the position specified by the cordites after the command. The rate of movement is the fastest possible for a certain machine.

Reset - Reset key on the CNC controller allow to reset the control after an error or emergency situation.

RS-232 - Standard for serial communication transmission of data. Most of the CNC machines have a RS-232 communication port that can be connected to a computer or network.

RS-274 - Standard for CNC program code developed by the Electronic Industries Alliance (EIA), allowing the same code to run on different machines.

Sequence Number - Same as Block Number. Sequence numbers begin with an N followed by a number. Usually, the increment for next line number is 5 or 10 be able to insert new lines later. See Block Number.

Serial port - see RS-232.

Subroutine - A small program with its own program number called the main program, usually several times. It is commonly used when there are repetitive operations to reduce the size of the main program.

Syntax - The rules of structure that must be followed when writing in a specific language; grammar. CNC code the syntax rule must be followed, or it may cause program error or unexpected motion.

Tape - A perforated paper (with series of holes) or magnetized medium (with magnetized particles) for storing CNC code.

Text file - See ASCII format.

Thread depth - The perpendicular distance (height) between the crest and root of thread teeth.

Tolerance - An allowable amount of variation of the specified dimension of a part. It is defined in the drawing of the part to be machined.

Tool Nose Radius Compensation - See Cutter Compensation.

Tool Offset - See Cutter Compensation.

Tool Path - This is the path that the cutting tip takes. If toll nose radius compensation is used, the tool path is that the center of the tool radius takes.

Tool Radius Compensation - Cutter Compensation.

Variable - For the CNC program, variables are the coordinate numbers in the program. Example: X120.5 Z-15.345.

Verification - Computer generated 3-D representations of CNC tool paths. Before transferring to the CNC machine, the cutter path program can be verified using CAM simulation software, for a specific machine, for tool collision, shape, precision, etc.

Word - Part of the programming code combination of a letter (address) with a number. Examples: G02, X1.250, M05.

Work offset - The distance from the machine zero to the work reference zero (origin) on each axis. It is calculated automatically by the CNC controller when the part origin is set.

Work Reference (Zero) Point - See Origin.

Work zero - See Origin.

Workpiece - Part to be machined.

Term	Description

Glossary Notes:

Index

Made in the USA
Monee, IL
19 November 2021

82535739R00150